10-82

P9-BYD-744

"We're Not Married, Alex!"

Alanna said. "I'm not a Knight."

"Not yet." Her protest was silenced by the lips which captured hers. Alanna was transported to a world encompassing only Alexander Knight.

In the delirium of that kiss she *was* a Knight, with every right to the luxuries he offered. His lips drank in her goodness; he moved against her with electrifying friction.

"Alex," she gasped against his cheek. "This has to stop."

"Why?" he whispered hoarsely. "Why?"

BILLIE DOUGLASS
enjoys writing romances and confesses that her "family, friends, and imagination" are her chief influences. She spends hours researching at the library—and in "backseat traveling"—for new interesting locations.

Dear Reader,

Silhouette Special Editions are an exciting new line of contemporary romances from Silhouette Books. Special Editions are written specifically for our readers who want a story with heightened romantic tension.

Special Editions have all the elements you've enjoyed in Silhouette Romances and *more*. These stories concentrate on romance in a longer, more realistic and sophisticated way, and they feature greater sensual detail.

I hope you enjoy this book and all the wonderful romances from Silhouette. We welcome any suggestions or comments and invite you to write to us at the address below.

Karen Solem
Editor-in-Chief
Silhouette Books
P.O. Box 769
New York, N. Y. 10019

BILLIE DOUGLASS
Knightly Love

Silhouette Special Edition
Published by Silhouette Books New York
America's Publisher of Contemporary Romance

Other Silhouette Books by Billie Douglass

Search for a New Dawn
A Time to Love

SILHOUETTE BOOKS, a Simon & Schuster Division of
GULF & WESTERN CORPORATION
1230 Avenue of the Americas, New York, N.Y. 10020

Copyright © 1982 by Barbara Delinsky

Distributed by Pocket Books

All rights reserved, including the right to reproduce
this book or portions thereof in any form whatsoever.
For information address Silhouette Books, 1230
Avenue of the Americas, New York, N.Y. 10020

ISBN: 0-671-53558-7

First Silhouette Books printing November, 1982

10 9 8 7 6 5 4 3 2 1

All of the characters in this book are fictitious. Any resem-
blance to actual persons, living or dead, is purely coincidental.

Map by Ray Lundgren

SILHOUETTE, SILHOUETTE SPECIAL EDITION
and colophon are trademarks of Simon & Schuster.

America's Publisher of Contemporary Romance

Printed in the U.S.A.

Knightly
Love

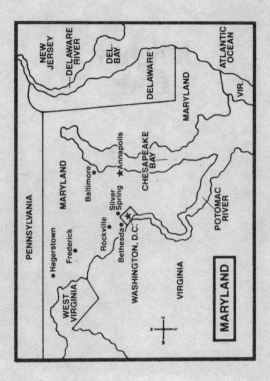

Chapter One

The fiery embers of sunset blazed their reflection across the glass-fronted structure, joining Alanna Evans' own slender reflection as she crossed the parking lot of the medical center's newest wing and entered its lobby. Her honeyed head held high with confidence, she approached the elevator, pushed the up button and waited.

After a day of nonstop business she welcomed the moment's pause and breathed deeply to savor it. All sound was subdued in the quiet lobby. A faint hum of conversation trickled from the lounge to her right, the intermittent beeping of the hospital paging system echoed from the reception desk to her left and the muted rustle of a passing white-garbed practitioner served to emphasize the stark immobility of the shiny doors before her.

She dropped her gaze to look through the lighter bottom of her tinted glasses to the deep blue carpet, against which her gray pumps looked properly subtle. Absently, she straightened the soft pleats of her skirt, adjusted its matching jacket, then shifted her overnight bag to rest the strap more comfortably on her shoulder. As the purr of the elevator signaled its approach a man joined her silently, standing perfectly still. Her peripheral vision absorbed no more than his remarkably tall, dark-suited form before a gentle chime heralded the elevator's arrival. Seconds later, the door slid open.

Moving simultaneously, both prospective passengers stepped forward. Then each paused to let the other pass. When a chivalrous hand gestured her forward, Alana smoothly entered, pressed the button for her floor, then turned to stand with her back to the wall. The man followed, glancing briefly at the single number already lit on the command panel before stationing himself opposite her in a stance both casual and alert.

With a soft thud the door closed and they were alone. Drawn by an enigmatic impulse, Alana looked across to meet his gaze head-on. His back rested lightly against the wall, his hands thrust in the pants pockets of his finely tailored suit. He seemed a study in contrasts —white shirt against dark gray wool, brown hair flecked with gleaming gold highlights, broad shoulders tapering to lean and narrow hips. And he continued to stare at her.

While Alanna was an unusually attractive woman, well used to the admiring glances sent her way by men and women alike, this particular glance was different. Even the subtly defiant tilt of her chin could not discourage it. Charcoal eyes, deep and intense, studied her closely, evaluating her much as she had done him and remaining uncomfortably persistent. With a cool determination born of practice she broke the contact, raising her eyes to the horizontal panel above the doors. Two. Three. Four.

The elevator glided to a gentle stop. As soon as the doors rolled open she straightened her shoulders and stepped forward. Again his movement paralleled her own. Again she halted, but this time it was Alanna who gestured, with an indulgent dip of her head, for the man to precede her. With an imperceptible nod, he stepped ahead, but not before she noted the distinct twitch of amusement at his lips. Her eye followed his broad back as he disembarked, turned and disappeared through a set of swinging doors to be swallowed up by the long hospital corridor beyond. Only then did she breathe deeply once more, bolstering her composure to approach the nearby nurses' station.

She stood patiently for a moment, respectful of the urgent nature of hospital business and slightly disconcerted by her own upcoming role here. The white-capped head before her was downcast, lost in the deciphering of scrawled doctor's orders. Finally, as if with the sudden realization of Alanna's presence, the nurse looked up.

"May I help you?"

"Yes, please. I'm Alanna Evans. I'll be participating in the IAT study. I believe Dr. Henderson is expecting me?"

Recognition lit up the nurse's face, her broad smile mirroring the white of her uniform as she stood and extended a warm hand, which Alanna clasped readily.

"Ms. Evans, welcome! I'm Sylvia Frazier, the night nurse heading the unit. We weren't quite sure just when you would arrive."

Reassured by the woman's friendliness, Alanna relaxed. "I wasn't quite sure myself. It's been a hectic day. Fortunately, I was able to escape from the office at seven." She glanced at the clock and noticed that it was barely seven-thirty; she had made good time.

"Then you haven't eaten?"

Alanna smiled ruefully. "No. But that's nothing new. I'd half hoped to be able to grab something in the cafeteria here, either before or after I spoke with Dr. Henderson. Is she free now?"

"I don't think so, dear." The older woman shook her head, then frowned. "I believe she may be with one of the other participants. Let me check."

Alanna's inner tension was betrayed only by the white knuckles gripping the strap of her overnight bag. Determinedly, she relaxed her fingers. Looking slowly around, she shuddered, for a fleeting moment recalling her past hospital experience, the long, painful vigil at her mother's bedside so many years ago. Mercifully, she herself had never been sick, truly sick, a day in her life. Her present problem was an annoyance more than anything else. A grave annoyance. As a woman who prided herself on self-command, she was frustrated.

Her attention snapped back to the present as Sylvia Frazier returned. "It's as I suspected. She'll be tied up for a little while. It's slow going at the start. Why don't you go down and have a good supper?" Her eye skimmed the slim figure before her with kind, almost maternal concern. "You could use several pounds, I'll warrant. But," she shrugged with a guilty grin, "perhaps that's just the envy in me speaking. I've been at the other end of that 'ideal weight' chart for too long. Run along now. I've told the doctor where you'll be. You can leave your bag here. And enjoy your dinner." She emphasized the words, smiling knowingly.

Given the circumstances, and the fact that they would be seeing quite a bit of each other, it was nice to know that Sylvia Frazier had a sense of humor. Alanna laughed. "That bad, eh?"

"Oh, not too bad . . . for institution fare. But it *is* institution fare."

"Any recommendations?" She arched a blond brow mischievously.

The nurse's choice was instant and from the heart. "Apple pie, à la mode." Then, catching herself, she feigned sternness. "After a healthy helping of chicken or fish, of course. Now, go!" Her gentle order was reinforced by the shooing motion of her hands. Alanna went.

Five minutes later, seated alone at a corner table in the sparsely filled cafeteria, she cast a plaintive glance at the junior sirloin before her. Had she really wanted it, or the fries and salad accompanying it? Or was she merely hoping for sustenance to help her through the night ahead?

Only after she took several perfunctory bites did she realize how hungry she was. When had lunch been? An eon ago. Or, to be precise, an executive board meeting, three separate conferences, two endless proposal forms and a dozen phone calls ago.

Slowly, as the meal before her disappeared, she

11

began to unwind. It might have been a trying day, but it had been a good one. Hard work was an integral part of her approach to life. Alanna thrived on it. Her penetration into the elitist ranks of the male-dominated executive level at WallMar Enterprises had been—contrary to recent rumor—the result of long hours, persistence, innate ability and sheer hard work. Realism held taut rein over bitterness in her musings; despite all recent advances against sexism, a woman still had to work *twice* as hard to achieve a niche comparable to her male counterparts in the corporate structure. But, it was worth it. As Vice-President of Development her days were challenging and rewarding, petty aggravations and innuendo notwithstanding. Why, then, her present dilemma?

Insomnia. Millions of Americans suffered from it, yet that fact held small solace when, in the middle of the night, she awoke to find sleep an elusive quality. The pattern was always the same. For no apparent reason her sound sleep would be shattered at one, perhaps two, in the morning. Tossing in bed, she would think, wonder, brood, awaiting the imminent slumber that grew less imminent with each passing moment. For the longer the wakefulness persisted—and it frequently lasted for two or three hours—the more annoyed she became, keying herself up in a way that denied sleep even further.

It was a self-perpetuating nuisance. And Alanna Evans was not one to suffer nuisances willingly, particularly one that rendered her groggy and irritable at seven o'clock each morning, when her alarm rang. Granted, her good nature was usually in order by the time WallMar saw her at eight-thirty, but as the day wore on it became harder and harder to maintain. A steady year of tension and exhaustion was enough; she had finally taken the offensive. Hence the IAT study.

Recalling her immediate purpose, Alanna sat back in her seat, nibbling on a thick steak fry as her eye skimmed the room. There were a scattering of hospital personnel in small clusters here and there and a fair share of visitors. There was also—her teeth clamped down into the soft potato and held—a man walking directly toward her, his dark suit, exquisite physique and daring height identifying him instantly. Had they not, his charcoal eyes would certainly have done so, for they captured her gaze with the same glittering depth and intensity she had fallen victim to in the elevator, and they held unwaveringly as he moved with animal grace through the maze of tables to her corner.

Who was he? Alanna felt a twinge of familiarity, yet she couldn't quite make the identification. Nor did she have time to ponder it for, too soon, the man reached her side. In his hands he held two cups of a steaming brew she half suspected to be his own secret potion. Without even sipping it, she felt under an inexplicable spell.

"I see you haven't had coffee. Will you join me?" His voice was as smooth as the rest of him. Alanna was entranced by his aura of command, so much so that she hadn't moved a muscle since she'd first seen him approaching. Now, snapping back to life, she bit through the steak fry and chewed slowly, pensively, as she regained her poise. What was it about this man which was so compelling? Almost from instinct, with years of training behind her, she steeled herself against his charm.

"I'm sorry," she answered calmly, rising to his subtle challenge, "but I don't drink coffee in the evening. It disturbs my sleep." When she would have looked away in dismissal she found herself challenged anew. For the smugness of her refusal brought an equally cocky smile to the face across from her.

"Then I'm glad I ordered it decaffeinated. Cream? Sugar?" Her headshake was meant as a refusal of his company, but he chose to make a different interpretation and the black coffee was beside her plate before she could protest. Deftly, the man eased his long frame into the chair opposite hers. "It seems we share the problem. How was your dinner?"

With this stranger now firmly ensconced at her table it occurred to Alanna that she'd been given absolutely no say in the matter. "Not bad," she spoke evenly, eying the man through her tinted lenses. "I was enjoying the solitude. Time to oneself is a precious thing nowadays."

"And I've shattered it . . . ?" Silvery sparks of humor glittered in his eyes.

"Let's just say you . . . intruded on it." This man needed no ego reinforcement; that he could easily shatter the peace of mind of many a woman was a given. "Are you always this aggressive?"

"Not usually. Actually, I surprised myself right now. I, too, usually enjoy being alone when I have the chance . . . which isn't very often. Aggressive?" He frowned, seeming to consider the word. "Only when I want something badly enough."

"You want something?" she asked innocently. She looked around in a mocking search. "I don't see much that's available. Am I missing something?" Underlying her tone was a streak of amusement. Alanna relished good verbal sparring; this man had the potential to be a worthy opponent. Not to mention the fact that his voice was deep and resonant . . . and very pleasing. . . .

"I believe you are," he countered, "but it's not your fault. You had no reason to be on the lookout for it in as improbable a setting as this. In time you'll understand."

Alanna took refuge behind the rim of her coffee cup, sipping slowly as she studied the stranger. By all rights she should ask him to leave. In fact, it surprised her that she hadn't. She sensed something different in him—something she had felt in the elevator that was even more pronounced now. There was an arrogance about him—but a depth as well. He challenged her.

"What *do* you see?" he asked, surviving her scrutiny unscathed.

Alanna put down her cup, shifted in her seat, and cocked her head in contemplation. "I see a man, perhaps thirty-seven or thirty-eight—"

"Thirty-nine."

"Thank you. Thirty-nine." She stifled a grin. "Tall—oh, say six-three or so?"

"Close enough." He nodded, smiling faintly.

"Weight . . . I won't even make a guess, since I'm no expert at that and since it's quite unimportant." She narrowed her gaze, fully involved in the game. "Athletic build, however. I'd guess you either work out regularly or play tennis—"

"Handball."

"That'll do." She smiled sweetly, feeling immune to his charm as long as she could describe him dispassionately. "Classic features—no, more rugged than classic. Brown hair with sandy highlights," she continued, glancing at the overhead light responsible for the last, "a nose that has been broken at least once, firm lips that express a distinct stubbornness," she grinned as the items in question twitched, "and eyes of charcoal gray that can be even more eloquent than that very glib tongue."

"No offense intended, of course?"

"Of course," she agreed drily, taking another sip of her coffee.

"Go on." Truly enjoying himself, he sat back in his chair, the fabric of his shirt stretching enticingly across his chest.

Alanna ignored the latter with a shrug. "What more is there to say?" She wasn't about to sum him up as perhaps the most handsome man she had seen in years, though it was the truth.

"Use your imagination," came his soft command. "I'm curious to see how the female mind sizes up its adversary."

"Adversary," she echoed. "Very good." So, he knew how she saw him, did he? Well then, she decided, she would let her imagination roam free. "All right." She cleared her throat. "I see a man used to giving orders without having them questioned."

"Would you question them?"

"You bet your life I would!" she flashed back with more vehemence than she had intended. Quickly she caught herself, steadying her voice. "I like giving an order or two myself on occasion. But that's beside the point," she added, reluctant to offer much about herself. "And speaking of that shirt, it *and* your suit are of very high quality—private tailor, perhaps?"

"Europe."

Alanna nodded, as though it were the most normal thing in the world. "Europe. I'm sorry I questioned that." A slender finger pushed her oversized glasses higher on the bridge of her nose. "Then, of course, you must be quite successful at what you do . . . to be able to shop in Europe. . . ."

He nodded, more modest than she would have expected. "I've been fortunate."

On the subconscious level, his vague familiarity got to her. Tilting her blond head, she frowned. "Do I know you from somewhere?"

"You're great!" he laughed softly, sparring still. "Isn't that supposed to be *my* line?"

"Tradition, my dear sir," she replied unfazed, "is irrelevant in this day and age. Well . . . ?"

"Well what?"

"Look." She sat forward with a sigh of impatience. "I really don't make a habit of talking to strange men."

Any discomfort she felt was totally her own. This strange man was quite pleased. "I'm glad to hear that. One less thing for us to argue about."

Alanna leaned down to retrieve her purse. She had begun to feel her control of the situation slipping and she was disquieted. "Please, either identify yourself or I'll be on my way." She paused. "Actually, I do have an appointment in another few minutes. Every game has

17

to come to an end and this one is beginning to wear thin." She paused, her cocoa gaze narrowing. "You walk around as though you own this place and everyone in it. It's a very subtle air—but very much present. Well, you don't own *me*. And I think you owe me the courtesy of an introduction."

His deep, charcoal eyes grew suddenly more serious, remaining as intense as ever. Formally extending his hand across the table, he introduced himself. "I'm Alexander Knight. Alex."

Alanna hesitated, yet somehow her slim hand found its way into his larger, stronger one, warmth spreading through her. Only after several moments did his identity sink in. And with the realization came a heightened flush of pink to her cream-soft cheeks. Her smile crept out unbidden. "So you *do* own the place—or practically. I understand that the new wing—the Knight Center —was your doing." Her hand remained in his. She was aware of the strength he exuded and found it strangely comforting.

"Only in part. My family made the original gift. The rest was the work of other donors and members of the hospital staff. They deserve most of the credit."

"Ah, such modesty," she chided, though her teasing was gentle, her voice soft. His smile was quite disarming—as was his touch. He continued to hold her hand, even faintly caress her fingers. Clearing her throat, she smiled. "My hand, please?"

He released it reluctantly, his eye falling to its partner with curiosity, even a certain tension. "No rings?"

"No."

"Husband?"

"No."

"Fiancé?"

"No." Her gaze now held his with confidence.

"Special guy?"

"No."

She didn't actually hear his sigh of relief when he paused, yet he chose his words with care. "Any particular reason? I mean, you *are* striking enough . . ."

She overlooked his compliment in the urgency of expressing her deepest feeling. "I'm unattached because I choose to be so. It's as simple as that . . . and as irrevocable." The last was added in warning; it had always been quite effective in the past. Now, however, it merely elicited a broad white grin from amid his tanned features.

"I'll enjoy seeing you eat those words one day."

"I doubt it." She was equally as calm and composed. "But," her pause was punctuated with a frown, "I'm curious as to why you seem so sure of that. You don't know anything about me."

"Well, then, we'll just have to do something about that, particularly since you're going to be my wife one day. . . ."

If he had expected an outburst of disbelief or indignation, even fury, he did, indeed, have much to learn about Alanna Evans. She was given to neither, particularly on a subject about which she felt so sure of herself. Her laugh was light and airy, as though it had flitted off the wings of a butterfly on a warm spring day.

"I may have a name for the face, now, Alex," she said melodiously, "but you're still *strange!* Whatever would put such a bizarre thought in your mind?"

"There's nothing at all bizarre about it," he returned, equally as good-humored, yet oddly sober. "You *will* marry me."

Again she laughed. "I've never heard anything so improbable! I don't know you, nor you me. You've never laid eyes on me before now. Besides, you happen to be talking to a confirmed bachelor-ess!"

"Even the most confirmed of bachelors can change." His dark gaze broke through her veneer of humor with its raw intensity. "I have."

"On a moment's notice?" Incredulity replaced amusement, covering up a more significant emotional spark.

"Not just a moment's notice." He spoke with a velvet tongue and frightening conviction. "I've had years to ponder who and what I want. I've never even caught sight of it . . . until now. And now that it's finally appeared I have no intention of letting it slip through my fingers."

"*It?* You sound as though you're referring to a business deal. If that's the case, this is one business that's not on the market."

"Perhaps not on the *open* market," he persisted softly, "but available, to say the least. It may just take you awhile to acknowledge it."

"You're incredible!" Her eyes widened. "You don't even know my name!"

"Ah-ah," he chided, "never underestimate the opposition. Your name is Alanna Evans . . . soon to be Knight."

For the first time Alanna felt threatened. If he had seemed less sure of himself, less arrogant, she might have taken it all as a joke. But this man was no crank if his reputation, or his family's, was worth anything. She was usually able to keep on top of things, yet the fact of hearing her name from Alex Knight's tongue was upsetting. Or, she wondered fleetingly, was it in the warm inflection that his tongue gave to it . . . ?

"How did you know that?" she asked, fighting for composure.

"Sylvia Frazier is a friend. And there aren't too many blond-haired beauties with owl-eyes who drop by the clinic at this hour." He paused, savoring the brief unsureness in her expression before directing his attention to her face. "Do you always hide behind them?"

Alanna frowned in puzzlement. "Behind what?"

"Those glasses. They're very large and, there at the top, the part through which you're glaring at me now, very dark. They must be convenient for hiding your emotions from the world. Are you frightened of what the world might see?"

To her chagrin, dark lenses notwithstanding, Alanna realized that she was glaring. Quickly she forced a smile. It was part of the game, she mused, meeting the challenge with a steady hand that reached up, slowly, toward the tortoiseshell frames. Smiling now in gentle defiance, she removed the glasses to reveal large eyes of a deep, soft brown.

"I wear these glasses for one basic reason," she

explained carefully, playing on his sense of expectance. Her pause was deliberate and drama-filled.

"And what might that be?"

"I'm nearsighted." The words flowed forth in a provocative drawl. Alanna grinned, then rose to the challenge as the man across from her presented several straightened fingers for her to count. "Three," she proclaimed proudly. "I'm not *that* bad, though I hope I'm not disappointing you. I *do* manage to live quite well with the weakness."

A mocking eyebrow rose. "I never doubted it for a minute. I'm just surprised you haven't tried contact lenses. Most women prefer—"

"I'm not most women. My glasses and I get along just fine." The object under discussion lay, temporarily forgotten, on the table.

"You have lovely eyes." His teasing tone was gone and Alanna's mouth felt suddenly dry. Though she sipped the last of her now-cooled coffee, she refused to let his relentless gaze intimidate her. Then, with the twinkle of an eye, his humor made a comeback. "It's actually gratifying to know that, while the world sees only your specs, I'll get to see the gems beneath."

"You presume quite a bit."

"Not without good reason."

He could match her, word for word, argument for argument. Though there was an undercurrent of teasing now, there was something else—something that gave Alanna pause.

"You *are* serious, aren't you?" she asked, puzzled, blunt.

Her bluntness was matched by his response. "Dead

serious. I intend to marry you." Everything in his expression—from the deep set of those charcoal eyes to the matter-of-fact angle of his head to the firm slant of his lips, which monopolized her gaze for a hypnotic moment—reinforced his earnestness.

Exasperated, she shook her head. "Please, Mr. Knight—"

"Alex!"

"Alex . . . you may be serious, but please believe that I am, too. I have no intention of marrying you or anyone else. My life is just fine the way it is."

"Is it?" He sat forward, challenging her afresh. "Is that why you're here? Is that why you can't sleep at night?"

Alanna stiffened. "I thought dealings with doctors were supposed to be confidential. Whoever is feeding you your information is out of line." The indignance in her tone was unmistakable. "And if you have any power at all in this hospital you should see that the breach is sealed."

"Perhaps," he drawled deeply, "it's precisely my power that caused the breach to begin with."

"Then it's that much less excusable!"

To her dismay Alex smiled, enjoying her unease. The warmth of his gaze melted her resentment, even against her will. "You really have nothing to worry about, Alanna. That's all I know—your name and your reason for being here. And there was no breach of confidence by any doctor; Sylvia spilled the last, as well. Anything further, I guess I'll have to ferret out of you. Believe it or not, this hospital *is* closemouthed."

"That remains to be seen," Alanna commented

wryly. Looking away, she caught the glint of the overhead light as it cast its tawny highlight on the fine hairs on the back of his hand. It was an image she thrust from her mind as being far too sensual, far too appealing. Grasping for an escape, she brightened. "Tell me . . . what can *you* learn from surface information? Since you don't know me, whatever makes you think you'd want me as a wife?"

"For starters," he began without hesitation, "I know that you're part of the IAT study—that was what Sylvia told me. It says a lot."

"Such as . . . ?"

"Such as that you're a working woman—a business-woman—at the executive level." At her look of surprise, he explained. "The IAT study—this phase, at least—deals with a very specific group. Executives. Under pressure. Between the ages of thirty and forty-five. I'd say," his gaze raked her form with astounding thoroughness, pausing longer on her lips before returning to the anticipation in her eyes, "that you are at the bare bottom of that scale."

"You're right. I just turned thirty-one."

"And *that* says a lot more."

"My age?"

"The fact that you offer it so freely. Some women are very sensitive—"

"I'm not *some* women."

"Which tells me even more. You're a nonconformist. You're self-confident, intelligent to have gotten where you are, and at least moderately aggressive."

"Moderately?" she asked, amused by his evaluation.

"Actually, with regard to the factor of aggression

you're still an unknown factor. You may be very aggressive in the office; in . . . ah . . . other fields you may not have been put to the test yet." The dark gleam which flickered in his eye spoke clearly of the fields he had in mind. Alanna's reaction was instant.

"Do you really think that you'll be the one to test me?"

"Perhaps."

"Don't hold your breath," she warned softly. "I've fought my way from the bottom up, parrying similar threats all too often. Fighting you would be no different than fighting those others who've tried before you."

Even as the words hit the air she wondered at their truth. From that first visual exchange in the elevator she had sensed something different in this man. A fight with him would push her to her limits, of that she was certain. Would it come to that? Despite his claims and her renunciation of them, would she be seeing him again?

"And that's another thing I like about you," he went on, totally ignoring her declaration. "You've got spunk. That's good."

"You're nuts! Do you know that?"

He chuckled. "I've been told so on occasion—but I've usually gone on to prove myself totally sane. Are you interested in putting me to the test?"

"What test—proving you sane?" When he shook his head with deliberate slowness she amended her guess, once again with disbelief. "Marrying you?"

"Ummm." His gaze began to move over her face in a visual caress that was utterly sensual. Beginning with her flaxen-sheened hair, pulled sedately back, his eye-touch stroked the creamy richness of her skin, the delicate symmetry of her nose, the sudden vulnerability of her lips. Awareness coursed through her in echoing ripples.

"I told you," she argued defensively, her stiff tone belying the helpless cocoa of her eyes, "that I'm not the marrying type. Marriage has nothing to offer me that I don't already have."

"Which brings me to my original question. Why do you have insomnia?"

"Insomnia has nothing to do with marriage," she asserted boldly.

"No, but if your life is as perfect as you seem to feel, you shouldn't have insomnia. What causes it?"

Exasperated once more, Alanna sighed. "If I knew the answer to that I wouldn't be here right now. In fact, I'm not quite sure why I *am* sitting here listening to you!"

"You're listening to me," Alex informed her without a second's pause, "because I challenge you. Because I don't 'yes' you all over the place, as I'm sure most of the men you're used to dealing with do. Because I dare to question you. Because I interest you."

He was right. She could simply have stood and excused herself when he arrived at her table, and certainly immediately after he popped his half-baked notion that she would one day be his wife. Yet he *did* interest her . . . and he was obviously interested *in* her. With a quivering in her limbs that she would have liked to attribute to fatigue but could not, Alanna knew she had to leave. Standing quickly, she shouldered her purse and reached for her glasses, slipping them deftly onto her face.

"I really must go, Alex. I have an appointment." She glanced at her watch and saw, to her horror, that she'd been a full forty-five minutes in the cafeteria. "Oh, no, she'll be waiting."

"She'll find something to keep her busy," Alex drawled. He, too, had risen and made to escort her. "I presume you *are* talking about Ellen Henderson?"

Alanna was too aware of Alex's closeness to react naturally to this knowledge of her. Quickening her step, she nodded. "That's right."

"Then I'm very happy that Ellen is a *she*. I'm not sure I'd enjoy having you pour your heart out to a *him*. Unless it was me, of course. I tend to be the jealous type."

As they reached the door of the cafeteria Alanna turned to face him. "Alex, it was nice meeting you, but I really have no time to continue the game. My life is filled to bursting as it is. I hope that you can simply put this weird compulsion of yours out of your mind. We'd both be healthier."

"Would we?" Taking her arm, he guided her in the direction of the elevator, holding her gently but firmly until the car arrived, entering with her and pushing the button for the proper floor. As fate would have it there were, again, no other passengers. After the door blocked out the rest of the world he looked down at her. "I think you're wrong. This is the healthiest thing *I've* done in years."

Without a further word he drew her to him, his hands

grasping her arms, his head lowering. She hadn't expected such suddenness. Stunned, she had no time to muster a protest before his lips touched hers. They were warm and gentle, as teasing as his nature. She stood perfectly still, refusing to yield to the pressure as it increased, yet unable to pull away. When teasing turned to seduction she struggled harder to remain indifferent. For, as with everything else about this man, his kiss, too, was different. His lips were vibrant, smoothly awakening her long-dormant senses. The warmth that began in her toes inched slowly upward, slowly and with growing heat as it made its way through her limbs. Her fingers itched to touch, her lips to respond. But his arrogance stayed her; she would no more give in to his cocksure demand than she would agree to his absurd marriage declaration. In the next instant, however, he slyly altered the ground rules.

"Bet you can't do it," he drawled softly against her lips.

"Do what?" she whispered, tipping her head back to study him.

"Kiss me with everything you've got . . . then turn and walk away."

Alanna felt abruptly light-headed. She loved a challenge and this was the perfect out. She could maintain her dignity and meet his dare, all the while giving in to the very tempting lure of his male-strong lips. While a small, private voice within asked if *she* was the crazy one for what she was about to do, that more husky public voice accepted. "You've got yourself a bet."

As though squaring off for a wrestling bout, Alex dropped his arms to his sides. Beaming indulgently down on her, he waited. Alanna's hands found their way to his shoulders, then around to his back, exploring his strength as she brought her lips tentatively to his. With a mixture of curiosity and growing boldness she pressed sensuously against him—then caught her breath and pulled back in reaction to both the heady jolt of excitement that coursed through her veins and the opening of the elevator door.

Mercifully, there was no one on the other side to witness her momentary loss as she grappled for the poise that had been suddenly shattered. "Oops," she gasped. "It looks like . . . we've been . . . thwarted. . . ."

"Saved by the bell is more like it," he countered with a knowingly wicked smile. "Come on." A strong arm about her shoulder pulled her from the elevator.

"Where . . . ?" Numbly, she kept pace; she literally had no choice. They moved a few yards to the fire door, then through it, to the stairwell. "Alex, what are you doing?"

"I don't think I can stand the suspense. You have a point to prove, I believe." He moved her gently against the wall, satisfactorily placing the breadth of his back as a shield against any unwanted intrusion. "Now," he cleared his throat, "that kiss . . . ?"

"But . . . I *did* kiss you."

"Ah-ah. That was no kiss," he teased, his tone seductive in itself. "That was a taste . . . a peek. Now I want the real thing. The bet wasn't for a half-kiss; it was for a whole-kiss."

Alanna was caught up in more than one game, for to their verbal sparring had been added the factor of raw physical need. Tingles deep within her attested to it. "There's a difference?" she floundered, buying time, hiding her growing turmoil in mock innocence. If that had been a half-kiss, she mused with alarm, she'd never have a chance in the world of winning the bet. This man had a touch, no doubt about it. She'd never been so affected before. Even now, as her hesitant gaze met his, she felt the draw. In her knees. Her chest. The deepest nooks and crannies of her body. All seemed suddenly aroused.

Alex moved closer, a long forefinger stroking her cheek. "Oh, there's a difference, owl-eyes," he murmured, seemingly entranced by her lips. "Let me demonstrate."

If only she had pulled away then, *before* his demonstration, she might have saved herself. But she was mesmerized, held immobile by his hands, drugged by the manly scent that encompassed him as surely as his aura of command, and lost in, yes, a web of sheer desire.

Alanna Evans was not an inexperienced woman. Yet Alex's touch was new, his kiss exciting, his nearness an intoxicant she had never before known. Now, as his lips gently sampled hers, slanting tentatively across them, coaxing them apart with subtle promises, she had no wish to resist. Rather, her nascent response was an invitation to a depth of passion she could only imagine. A shudder ran through her at the touch of his tongue exploring the curve of her lips and the softness within. If her knees grew weak, it was of no import. For his arms circled her, drawing her from the wall and against the long, hard-muscled support of his body.

The moment was isolated in eternity in Alanna's wheeling mind. She felt overwhelmingly alive and fresh, electrically charged, drawn from dormancy to heaven. Her arms stole beneath his to his back, her hands reveling in the corded strength there.

Then her pulse hammered loudly as he leaned back. His smoky gray eyes studied her indolently, savoring the flush on her cheeks. "Now it's your turn," he whispered, a deeply crooned challenge. Holding his face just so far from hers, he demanded that she take the initiative to steal another kiss.

Alanna was powerless against the drive stirring within her. Her usual manner was neither coy nor hesitant. She had always been honest with herself. When she wanted something, she went after it. And, at that moment, she wanted to kiss Alex Knight, to push that budding passion even further. Eagerly she leaned closer, her slender body as pliant against his manly lines as layers of raw silk draped across a bronze statue. Her lips parted in search of his, reaching, playing only until she felt his ragged gasp, then, forgetting play, moving in nearer, deeper, harder.

Neither Alex nor Alanna was aware of the door opening not far from them. A throat cleared. "Excuse me . . ." A forced cough. "Ah . . . Mr. Knight . . . excuse me . . . Ms. Evans . . ."

Alanna wasn't quite sure when she finally recognized the presence of a third person. Alex, however, recovered sooner. Though his arms held her still, he raised his head.

"Yes, Sylvia?" he asked thickly.

Sylvia Frazier cleared her throat once more before

speaking in stage whisper which carried a hint of chiding. "Dr. Henderson is waiting to see Ms. Evans. I saw you two get off the elevator. I really think—"

"Thank you for the reminder, Sylvia." Alex didn't turn. His gray eyes glittered into Alanna's with a pointed message and, slowly, she grasped reality. She felt the rapid rise and fall of her chest, the pounding of blood through her veins, the eerie weakness in her legs. But there was, still, that last part of the bet. . . .

Straightening, she took a deep breath. "I'm coming now, Ms. Frazier. Please tell Dr. Henderson that I'll be right along." As Alanna gently extricated herself from Alex's arms the nurse diplomatically disappeared, her job done. But Alex's strong hand stayed Alanna before she, too, could return to the floor.

"You lose, you know," he grinned mischievously. "If Sylvia hadn't come along just then you wouldn't have left." He paused, his nearness continuing to affect her. As she looked up at him his gaze grew enigmatic. "Would you?"

A smile tugged at the corners of her lips as she lifted her golden head a bit higher. While she refused to admit defeat, she could not lie. "We'll never know, will we?"

But the sureness of Alex's answer made a mockery of her smugness. "Oh, *we'll* know. And *you* can bet on *that!*"

With a hard swallow, Alanna turned and left.

Chapter Two

&llen Henderson was the antithesis of the ivory-tower psychologist. She was young, perhaps a year or two older than Alanna. She was attractive, tall and dark-haired, and dressed in a casual wool shirt-dress and high-heeled pumps. She was warm, compassionate and extremely goal-oriented. Alanna felt an instant rapport with her.

"I'm thrilled that you've agreed to be part of the study." She welcomed Alanna with a sincere smile, as the latter took the chair offered by her desk.

Alanna spoke honestly. "*I'm* glad that you may be able to help me. It's a frustrating problem."

"Of course it is! Hopefully, through your participation in the study, we'll *all* sleep better. It's just a beginning . . . as is so much of work done in sleep labs such as this."

"Can you tell me something, in general, about the study?" Alanna asked, recalling that Alex Knight knew that much more than she did.

Ellen grinned her understanding. "Sure. Let me explain, first off, that there are many different types of sleep problems. The three major ones affecting adults are narcolepsy, sleep apnea and insomnia. The narcoleptic may sleep well at night but falls into helpless sleep-stupors at odd points during the day, often in the midst of crucial activities. A victim of sleep apnea actually stops breathing up to four hundred times in the course of the night; only his body reflexes jolt him back to life. Needless to say, his sleep is constantly disturbed. Sudden Infant Death Syndrome is an early form of this. Then," she paused for a breath, her expression softening, "there's insomnia—the inability either to fall asleep at all or to fall back to sleep once awoken. Of the fifty million Americans afflicted with sleep troubles, thirty million have insomnia."

"Of which I am one."

"Unfortunately, yes."

"What causes it?"

Ellen sighed. "There may be any of a number of causes. A few are physical—but the physical exam Dr. Ramirez, our neurologist, gave you when you came in two weeks ago ruled out any gross physical problem. You're in excellent health." Her eyes fell to the folder opened on her desk. "You don't smoke?"

"No."

"Drink?"

"Other than the occasional cocktail or glass of wine, no."

"Take any medication to help you sleep?"

"No." She spoke softly, almost apologetically. "I

hate to take pills, period. I like to think that I have enough internal discipline to overcome any minor headaches." Her smile held regret. "Unfortunately, I don't have the discipline to control *this* problem."

"You will," Ellen assured her confidently. "That's what we'll be working on here."

Now they were down to the immediate situation. "What *will* I be doing?"

"Well, we have two weeks to work with. Fourteen nights. You *are* free of other obligations for that stretch, aren't you?"

Alanna answered easily. "I had several engagements, but after Dr. Ramirez called I was able to reschedule them."

"Good." The psychologist nodded. "Since we'll be concentrating on behavior modification, it's important to have the time. But," she paused, "let me backtrack a bit before I explain the specifics. The IAT—Insomnia Analysis and Treatment—study is a far-reaching one. We've identified many different types of people with insomnia. Your group, with its own specific characteristics, is only one."

Alanna couldn't help but quote what she'd learned earlier. "Executives. Under pressure. Between the ages of thirty and forty-five."

"Ah, you've been prompted?" Ellen grinned, not at all bothered.

"I met a fellow named Alex Knight in the cafeteria."

Ellen's grin broadened. "Yes, Alex. His family has been wonderful to us."

"So I gather." She also wondered whether Alex Knight had been wonderful to Ellen Henderson, then chided herself for her cattiness. She held her tongue as Ellen continued.

"He does know his facts. Those are the basic qualifications. The theory is that you people—we have four of you here at a time—suffer from insomnia as a result of the pressures you face relating to your careers. All of you are single, which rules out marital tension. All of you live alone, which rules out a bedmate who may disturb your sleep with snoring, restlessness, nightmares—that sort of thing."

Alanna ingested it all, yet her mind rushed on. "Why is the study being done *here?* Why the necessity of sleeping at the hospital?"

"It's a good question, and one I've had to answer repeatedly. What with hospital costs, you'd think this to be extravagant. I admit that it may be unorthodox, but if the field is to make significant advances, this type of study is a must. You see," she went on, "we'll be trying to control your environment, to keep that much more accurate an eye on your surroundings and sleep habits than we might be able to do if you were at home."

Alanna's thoughts shifted to the conversation she'd had with the neurologist and she felt a twinge of unease. "Dr. Ramirez mentioned some very complicated-sounding monitoring devices. Am I in for something awful?"

"No!" Ellen's appreciative laughter was instantly reassuring. "Tonight will be the only night you'll be wired up—"

"Wired up?"

"Nothing to worry about." Again the psychologist

soothed her. "We'll be monitoring your brainwaves, your heartrate and your body temperature."

Alanna's brow furrowed. "I'm not sure I understand. If you've ruled out any physical problem—"

"We have. These measurements are all related to sleep patterns. We'd like to establish, at the start, that you do go through the normal four stages of the sleep cycle. I'm sure you're familiar with the term. For the average adult the sleep cycle repeats itself many times throughout the night. Once we've plotted your sleep pattern I'll be able to show you a graphic illustration."

Alanna's lips twitched in humor. "I'd like to see that. With the number of finance and production charts I read in a day I often wonder whether I can see things any other way."

"Then you'll appreciate the illustration." Ellen smiled. "I don't actually anticipate seeing anything unusual, but it's necessary to find out if we're going to the effort of controlling so many other factors *and* taking two weeks' worth of your nights."

"Of course. I understand." Feeling slightly more comfortable about the monitoring, Alanna was curious again. "What then? What about the other thirteen nights?"

"OK." Ellen sat forward. "Now we get to the nitty-gritty of the project. We ask you to come in every night at roughly the same time, preferably no later than nine. Early curfew," she quipped, successfully coaxing Alanna into mirroring her smile. "We have a lounge in the unit and a small kitchen. Both are well appointed, very pleasant. You will have your own bedroom and a private bath—nothing fancy, but, again, pleasant. It will be dark and quiet. There will be no disturbances. Please sleep in whatever nightwear you're accustomed to. Above all, I want you to be comfortable. You may spend your evening until you fall asleep either in the lounge or in your room. Follow your usual routine. If you usually shower before bed, do it. When—and only when—you're sleepy, you'll go to bed. You will be woken at the same time every morning, regardless of that bedtime, and you will be expected to follow a fixed routine immediately after waking up—preferably some form of exercise, then breakfast." She paused, again consulting the papers on her desk. "I understand you swim?"

Alanna nodded. "I coach a swim team on Saturdays. Ten- to twelve-year-olds. Girls." At the thought, she brightened. "They're great kids!"

"Do you swim much on your own?"

"When I have the chance."

"Well," the psychologist drew out her words with feigned sternness, "I want you to *make* the chance. There's a pool just down the street which we have access to. If you'd like, you can swim every morning before breakfast."

Alanna knew only too clearly her prebreakfast moods. "I don't know, Ellen," she hesitated. "My early mornings are pretty bad. . . ."

"Then this will be one way of letting out all that pent-up aggression."

Aggression. That word again. Alanna couldn't help but remember when she'd heard it last. Then it had been on taunting male lips, firm and enticing. . . . Ellen snapped her from the memory.

"Will you try it? You may notice a huge improvement—both in your temperament *and* in your sleep habits."

The last did it. Though skeptical, Alanna was game. "I'll try."

"Great!"

"Ah . . . what else am I going to have to do?" Her good-natured, but wary, question was enough to lighten Ellen's expression even more.

"Nothing painful." She laughed. "We'd like to eliminate stress from the bedroom. That means no heavy reading or television while in bed. Staying in bed *only* while you're sleepy. Getting up and leaving the bedroom whenever you're unable to fall asleep—or back to sleep—quickly."

Alanna mulled over the suggestions. "Sounds fair."

"You don't nap during the day, do you?"

"If only I had time!" Her eyes widened in surprise.

"Well, don't!" the other woman rejoined just as quickly. "Never nap during the day—even on weekends. And no coffee or liquor after, say, three in the afternoon. OK?"

"Fine." She'd been doing as much already.

"One other thing, though I'll speak more about it tomorrow night when you come in. This is a self-help program. We'll be teaching you techniques of self-relaxation. You know, deep breathing, muscle-relaxing, mind-clearing."

"Interesting. . . ." It had never occurred to Alanna to do that.

"It will be, and it should help. I'll be on duty every night, should you want to talk. And there will be the other participants. You'll meet them tomorrow as well."

"But . . . what will I have to do with them?" This was a totally new thought.

Again Ellen was well prepared for the question. "I like to see this as a kind of halfway house. You may have *no* cause to talk with the others. But they're here with a problem similar to yours. The therapeutic value of talking with others can often be greater than talking with me."

"I see." She pondered the possibility. As a loner, she was hesitant. "Are they all from the greater-Baltimore area, too?"

"Uh-huh. There are two men and two women. I dare say you may find you're already acquainted with one or two." If she knew something Alanna didn't, there was no time for guessing. "You may even develop legitimate friendships." The doctor glanced at her watch. "Which reminds me, I still have to brief two more. Let me explain what else I want you to do."

"There's more?" Alanna had begun to feel saturated.

"Just a little." Ellen opened a drawer and withdrew an official-looking notebook with several blank charts in front. "I want you to keep a running log of your thoughts and activities from the time you arrive here at night until the time you leave in the morning. There is also a place to summarize your feelings about each day. I'm interested in general problems, aggravations. At night I want you to enter your periods of sleep *and* wakefulness. For the latter, concentrate on your thoughts upon awakening. If you leave the log here during the day I can go over it to keep pace with your progress." She paused, then grinned sheepishly. "Sound awesome?"

Alanna grinned wryly. "I suppose I've faced greater challenges." *Challenges.* Where had she heard *that* word before? Her grin faded quickly.

"I'm sure you have. And, considering your corporate achievements, I'm sure you'll meet this one as well."

It was a compliment that Alanna accepted graciously, if with mild embarrassment. After all, Ellen Henderson must have received her share of accolades to be in the position she now held.

"Any other questions, or would you like me to show you to your room?"

Sorting it all out, Alanna grew apprehensive. "Ah . . . tonight. When I'm all wired up, what happens if I wake up in the middle of the night?"

"If you lie awake for more than ten minutes ring for Sylvia. She'll unhook everything so you can get up. Walk around. Go into the lounge. Help yourself to some milk in the kitchen. Read a light magazine or a book. Pure escapism. Concentrate on relaxing. Don't go back to bed until you're really sleepy. You could try filling out the log." She patted the notebook with a knowing glance. "That's bound to put you to sleep!"

By the time Alanna had been shown over the lab and then to her room it was nearly ten. Not only was she armed with her log and sleep charts, but Ellen had given her questionnaires to complete, full of in-depth items relating to her childhood, her upbringing, her educational and occupational histories. Settling into the easy chair by the darkened window, she sighed. Exhaustion had its way of creeping up, suffusing weariness through her body. Perhaps she had been more tense about this than she had imagined. Her lips curved into a wry grin. When it came to the office she was in her element, able to face most every problem with aplomb. Something like this—a more personal situation—was another matter.

The pile of forms lay unheeded on her lap as she looked around the room which would be hers for the next two weeks. It was small, but as pleasant as Ellen had said it would be. Painted a pale blue, rather than the traditional hospital white, its simplicity was relaxing. A small table stood to her left, a dresser to her right. Against the far wall was a nightstand, then the bed. In this case, too, white had been usurped by the pale green of both sheets and blankets. The warm glow of the lamp on the nightstand blended with a floor lamp by her chair to bathe the room in a light as gentle as that of dawn. To her surprise, Alanna felt quite comfortable.

Turning to the first of the forms, she searched her purse for a pen, then began. The starting questions were standard. Name: Alanna Lyn Evans. Address: 2201 North Bancroft. Phone: 555–8821. Age: 31. Sex: Female. Marital Status: Single.

A yawn escaped unhampered. Ellen was right; the task was more effective than counting sheep. Mustering her discipline, Alanna returned to it.

Place of birth: Pittsburgh. Parents: Willard and Elizabeth Evans. Siblings: None.

At the second yawn, Alanna put down the pen. The

thought of outlining childhood illnesses and traumas, of which there were few, held no excitement. None at all.

Excitement. The word was a trigger, flashing an instant image before her mind's eye of a man, tall and broad-shouldered, arrogant as they come. Alexander Knight. Aside from the puppy love she had felt for Shep Harding, Alanna had never been stirred by a man in quite this way. Even aside from his preposterous mention of marriage, he was a puzzle. What coincidence had brought them together tonight? Had it only been for a few hours that she'd known of his existence?

Strange, she mused, how time could take on altered dimensions. It was as though she had known him much longer. Indeed, their kiss had borne an intimacy that shocked her. What had happened to her usual defenses?

Alanna kicked off her shoes and stood to explore the room. Her tapered fingers, their nails well shaped and clear, skimmed the curved edge of the tabletop, then the windowsill, bridging the gap to the bed, marking its length and width before falling to her side.

Would she see him again? He knew where to find her. But what did she know of him, save that he was part of *the* Knight family? His dress and manner spoke of dignity, of class; why, then, his ludicrous idea about marriage? He had been serious! Or had he been? Perhaps he was toying with her; maybe the rich and privileged were accustomed to joking that way. Could he have meant it—that he intended to marry her? The remembrance of the touch of his lips on hers came unbidden to mind. An intoxicating spice—a manly mystique—an insidious explosion of warmth within her. Was she that vulnerable, after all she had led herself to believe?

No! With a determined vow she turned to the closet and began to undress. Alex Knight might have been different, but she was not. She was the same Alanna Evans who had walked toward the hospital today with her head held high. She was a professional woman. She'd worked hard to get where she was. There was time for neither romance nor marriage in her life.

Standing before the dresser in her bra and slip, she reached to carefully remove the pins which had anchored her hair sedately through the day. With the removal of each pin a strand of flaxen silk fell over her pale shoulders, one, then another, until a rich mane of honeyed treasure cascaded to midback. She ran her fingers freely through its length, bending to her overnight bag for her brush, then stroking the fall of hair until it was glossy in the pale light. Once again she thought of Alex Knight and her fingertips feather-touched her lips. How delightful he had tasted, she mused, then grimaced. *Anything* might taste good after decaffeinated coffee!

Forcing her thoughts to her immediate plight, she showered, dressed in her nightgown and robe, then returned to her chair and the paperwork awaiting her. Again, instant sedation. Eyelids heavy. Sleep imminent. Within minutes she had pressed the call button and Sylvia Frazier was with her, bearing a cartload of paraphernalia which, under normal circumstances, would have frightened *anyone* out of sleep. But Sylvia, as she insisted Alanna call her, was one step ahead of her apprehension, explaining every gismo, pinpointing every wire's purpose and destination, reassuring Alanna until she felt no alarm at all. Surprisingly, she was barely aware of the monitoring electrodes when, finally, she was alone once more in the darkened room, awaiting sleep. Within minutes she had succumbed to its sweet, if temporary, escape.

It was shortly after two that the familiar internal alarm roused her. Blinking into the darkness, she struggled for several moments to identify her surroundings. With recollection came an ironic relief. What if, after claiming to have insomnia, she had slept like a babe through the night? Would they have thought her a fraud?

Fraud. It was a word that had been used all too often by a few skeptics to spread their ugly gossip. Perhaps it had been inevitable. From her earliest days at WallMar Enterprises she had kept all professional relationships strictly that—except for her friendship with Jake Wallace. A rapport had arisen between them from the start. Alanna found him to be intelligent and open, eager for her input and a far cry from so many of her more ambitious and competitive colleagues. Jake had no need for pettiness. As president of the company, his power was secure. When he promoted Alanna from Administrative Assistant to Director of Management in six short months no one had questioned him—to his face. Alanna had been all too aware of the subtle innuendos, however, the sly looks, even the leering glances. They all pointed to one supposition: that she was daringly sleeping her way to the top of the ladder.

Even now, in the darkness of her hospital room, Alanna felt the surge of anger which raced through her every time she brooded on the injustice of the accusation. One colleague, a young and rather rash man, had voiced the sentiment quite succinctly. "I only wish," he had drawled, raking her slender curves lewdly, "that I had the qualifications *you* have."

Alanna's way had been to ignore the taunts and turn the other cheek in an attempt to demonstrate that it had been by merit alone that she had earned her promotion. The charges were absurd. Jake Wallace was a balding man in his late fifties. Yes, she did adore him—and he adored her. She also adored his wife, who was confined to a wheelchair, and had spent many an evening with them both—none of which helped, since no one quite knew what went on inside the old and gracious Victorian mansion that had been in the Wallace family for years. Perhaps they thought of her as the daughter they'd never had. In her professional outlook she was certainly the son they'd never had. And Jake and Elaine were as close to family as *she* now had. Their friendship was mutually gratifying.

Ten minutes. Ellen had told her to get up if she lay awake for longer. It had been fifteen and she was tense and annoyed. Her frustrated summons for Sylvia was met quickly. Soon she was out of bed and, tying her robe securely around her, headed for the lounge and the hope of a diverting magazine. She'd have to remember to bring a book for tomorrow night. Blast! Why did she have to wake in the night to . . . this?

The lounge was quiet and deserted. Alanna had her choice of several easy chairs and finally sank onto the only sofa and stretched out her long legs. Her feet were bare; she'd forgotten to get slippers. She'd have to buy a pair tomorrow. Bare feet were the rule at her own place, where thick carpets always beckoned. Yet it was warm here and she made herself comfortable.

The minutes slowly ticked away as she turned page after page of the magazine. Finally, bored, she put it down, tossing her glasses onto the table beside her. What had Ellen said about self-help and learning to relax? Mustering her imagination, she rested her head on her arm and concentrated her gaze on the beige carpet, determinedly forcing all thoughts from mind. Inhaling deeply, she focussed her attention on this mental void, willing her limbs to languor, her pulse to steadiness. It worked. Like the slow breakup of clouds on a rain-misted morning, a tentative peace seeped through her. With each deep breath her tension eased until she felt, at last, sleepy. Her lids drooped, yet she was reluctant to move.

Aware of the world now only through the thick shade of her blond lashes, she found the intrusion of human flesh almost surreal. Only vaguely did the image register; as she slowly opened her eyes it sharpened. Human flesh—a pair of feet—masculine and tanned—connected to legs that were strong and roughened by light brown hairs. As she struggled to assimilate the presence it lowered itself calmly before her.

"Hi, pretty lady," a voice crooned with a deep resonance she would have recognized even had it not been imprinted on her memory so recently. In shock, she brought herself to full awareness. Her brown eyes widened to encompass the thick head of hair, sleep-mussed as was hers, the deep gray orbs which reflected her own image, the lips that were sensual and alive.

Forgetful of both the time and the surroundings, she cried in astonishment, "Alex!" Any further exclamation was drowned as his lips covered hers in a gentle greeting. She gasped, yet was, once again, powerless against his spell, savoring the sweet story his lips told so briefly. When she could breathe again she simply stared at him in amazement as he continued to kneel before her.

"What are *you* doing here at this hour?"

Amusement flitted dangerously in the gaze that swept her semiprone form. "The same thing you are."

"You're part of the study?" Was that possible? Was that why he had been here earlier? Was that the coincidence that had brought them together?

"Is that so hard to believe? I mean," he teased her wickedly, "I know that I may be handsome and witty and utterly irresistible during the day," he counted off the points, "but is it inconceivable that we share this problem as well?"

What else was it he had said they shared—their sense of challenge? It was a reminder that buoyed her through her confusion now. "You have insomnia?"

He nodded.

"No wonder you knew something about the study." Her thoughts were growing more lucid. "I more or less assumed that it was your family's role . . ."

Alex's expression tensed noticeably. "My family's position in this community, any power they may wield, is only incidental to my participation in the study."

It was, ironically, his vehemence that convinced her.

Earlier he had been in full command of his charm. Now, in the middle of the night, when they both should have been sleeping like so many of their peers, his shortened fuse was obvious. And she understood the feeling.

"I'm sorry. That came out the wrong way. I'm just so . . . surprised to see you here."

"Didn't I imply that we'd meet again?" He seemed to regain his humor as his gaze held hers steadily.

"You implied a lot more than that! I'd pretty much written you off as a crackpot!"

His grin was slow and enticing. "I do like your humor." He paused. "Couldn't sleep either?"

"Afraid not. I've been up for a while."

"Reading anything good?" His attention shifted momentarily to the now-forgotten magazine by her side.

"Very boring."

Without quite standing, he moved forward. "Move over. You've got the best spot." He took her shoulders to shift her before she could reposition herself. As he slithered into the corner where she had been she looked at him in alarm.

"Now *you've* got it. That wasn't very fair. I was there first."

"But you've got something even better." In graphic explanation he drew her against him, his body giving her far more exciting support than the sofa ever had. His arm curved around her shoulder; before she knew how her own settled across his middle and she rested comfortably against him. His warmth was as much a relaxant as her deep-breathing efforts had been earlier. Surprisingly, she didn't resist the lure.

"Comfortable?" he asked softly.

"Ummm." The scent of him was all male, filling her senses with a creeping euphoria.

Later she was to wonder at her complacency as she lay against Alex, a devastating stranger who had proposed marriage at their first meeting. Now, however, the silence was restorative, filled with a contentment that she savored, regardless of whatever afterthoughts she might have. His breathing was steady, his hands undemanding. At length he spoke with a resonance that flowed soothingly through her.

"I like you this way."

"What way?"

"Undressed."

Alanna tilted her head back, only realizing that he wore a burgundy-colored robe of thick terry as her cheek rubbed against it. "I'm not undressed," she contradicted him staunchly. "I am very properly covered by several layers of fabric."

"But soft. So very soft," he hummed against her hair. "And I like your hair down." His hand moved to gently explore its length. "It's like silk—golden silk."

"One hundred brushings a night and very hard to control at times," she quipped lightly, unable to accept the compliment with the pleasure she felt.

"That's why you wear it knotted back? For control?"

"Among other things."

"What things?"

The faint frown that brought her brows together was hidden as she relaxed her head once more. "It's hard enough projecting an image of efficiency and professionalism at the office without having a loose mop to cloud the issue."

"Ah." He caught her gist instantly. "Your male colleagues. Then I totally agree with you. By all means tie your hair up during the day. As long as you wear it down for me."

"Hmmmm," she chuckled. "No glasses. Long hair. You've got a nearsighted witch."

"A very beguiling one . . ." he drawled, his fingers tilting her chin up so he could study her face. "A very beautiful one . . ."

She was mesmerized, able only to return his gaze, devouring his good looks with helpless greed. Why was he *so* handsome? Or *was* it all physical? There was that aura again—one that surrounded his entire being with a sensuality she could not deny.

Her lips felt parched, her mouth dry. Every nerve end tingled with awareness. She felt herself sucked into the depths of those dark, charcoal eyes—sucked in and consumed, no longer a separate entity. Was that what life with Alex Knight would be like—the loss of the identity she had worked so hard to establish?

With a flash of fear she tried to pull away. But he held her firmly, refusing her bid to escape. "Don't go. I'm no threat to you." It was as if he read her mind. "If nothing more, indulge me. *You* know how maddening it is when you can't sleep. I'm more relaxed now than I've felt since I woke up."

The last thing she wanted was to leave, yet the strength of his power over her was disconcerting. As to his argument—hadn't Ellen suggested that the participants of the study might help each other? Perhaps, she mused, if there was some distance—*any* distance— between them . . .

"Just let me sit up," she suggested, her voice uncharacteristically wobbly. "I'll stay with you awhile."

His tone was mocking, yet he released her. "Not exactly what I had in mind, but, if I have no other choice . . ."

"You don't." Alanna sat now at arm's length. No part of their bodies touched yet, to her dismay, she was as aware of him as ever. Driven to break the bond of raw attraction that sizzled between them, she spoke quickly. "Tell me about yourself, Alex. I really know nothing about you."

One dark brow rose. "You did pretty well in the cafeteria."

"That was a game. Tell me something concrete. Like . . . like . . ." she grappled with sanity, ". . . like what you do for a living."

"I thought everyone knew." His dry statement puzzled her.

"That's the second reference you've made in the past few minutes to your family's reputation. Is that bitterness I detect?"

Alex thought for a moment, as though he had never been put to this test before. "Not bitterness. Let's just call it . . . resignation. I'm the third generation of my family in this area. It's often difficult to be preceded by someone else's reputation."

"I'm sure you meet the family standards," she offered in encouragement.

His gaze sharpened. "I meet *my* standards, or, at

least, I try to. But I like to be judged on my own merits, rather than those of my family. Do *you* come from a large family?"

Alanna was unaware of his deftness in shifting the conversation back to her until well after she'd fallen into the trap. "No. I had no brothers or sisters."

"Are your parents living?"

The painful memory forced her to avert her gaze. "They died years ago—my mother, when I was twenty, my father four years later."

"Then you're alone?"

She smiled thinly. "Alone . . . but not lonely, as the saying goes."

"You have friends?"

"My share. Mostly my work keeps me occupied."

"Tell me about your work."

Enough was enough. "Uh-uh. I asked you first. What do you do—every day?"

He looked at her evenly. "I head the Knight Foundation."

"Which means . . . ?"

"Which means that I have a finger in a lot of pies at any given time."

Alanna grunted. It was like pulling teeth to get the man down to specifics. Was he always this close-mouthed? Or simply with her? As though sensing her frustration, he yielded to her silent plea.

"Right now we're in the process of merging one of our electronics firms with two others. By forming a larger corporation we will have access to a nationwide network." The preoccupation of his gaze with her eyes suddenly ended. With slow deliberation he skimmed her neck and shoulders with his eyes, following the soft fabric of her robe to where her breasts swelled. Serious discussion was totally forgotten as Alanna felt the heat within herself begin to rise.

"Do you . . . ah . . . do the actual . . . negotiating . . . ?" She clutched at the conversation, fighting the honeyed currents which flowed around and about her.

His voice was low and at seductive odds with his words. "We have legal counsel for that. But *I* have to be on top of the legal counsel."

Her whispered "I see" fell victim to the web of arousal his gaze spun. His fingers moved to her shoulders, their tips drawing tiny circles on the silken gown.

"You look so pretty," he rasped as those fingers rose to thread through the hair that fell by her cheeks. "Do you always wake up looking like this—or did you do it just for me?"

"I didn't know you would be here!" she cried weakly, her sense of reason suddenly shaky. As his arm moved slowly to draw her closer she grew aware of its sinewed length, bared as it was to the elbow by the robe that barely reached to his knees. It had been bad enough when he had been fully dressed; *this* was sheer madness.

Alex had been right; she *was* different dressed like this. Her proper businesswear had been a shield, perhaps meager, but a shield nonetheless. In it she had known who she was and why she was here. Now she felt exposed—by far more than just the change of attire. Suddenly she felt unsure—and that made her angry. Moving quickly from his embrace, she stood.

"I think I'd better go to bed." Without looking back

she crossed the floor and headed toward her room. She had not gone far enough, however, to miss his low-murmured "Chicken." It stopped her in her tracks.

Head low, she took a breath. On its own a smile stole to her lips. He knew just how to manipulate her. That challenge . . . She simply could not turn down a challenge. Shaking her head in grudging admiration, she turned slowly to face him.

"What was that?" She cocked an eyebrow pertly.

Alex rose from the sofa and circled it to stand beside her. His eyes were dark with desire; it took every ounce of restraint for her to hold still. "I called you a chicken. You seem to take the easy way out when the going gets . . . hot."

Her hands found her waist. "I'm not taking the easy way out. I'm simply taking the smartest way. As I recall, we're here for a purpose." Her words were spoken in self-reproach as much as to the dark form towering above her. "A love affair in the middle of a hospital lounge is a little . . . tawdry." Miraculously, her voice remained steady, belying the quivering deep within.

"I couldn't agree with you more. Let's go. I'll put you to bed."

Before she could protest that arm was once more about her shoulders, burning through her nightclothes, fusing her to his side. Before she could withdraw they had reached her room. Before she could escape through its door—alone—he guided her in.

Then, before she could begin to argue, he pulled her into the circle of his arms. "This may be the best sedative in the world." And he kissed her.

Chapter Three

$\mathcal{N}$aked was a mild word for how Alanna felt. It had little to do with her scant covering and everything to do with the raw vulnerability Alex Knight had uncovered. Her senses were stripped of all defense by the powerfully tender persuasion of the lips that covered hers, the hard male body against which his arms molded her.

"Alex, don't . . ." she gasped when he abandoned her lips to rain havoc along the sensitive curve of her neck.

"Alanna, do . . ." he echoed against her ear, nipping its delicate lobe before slowly working his way back to her mouth. "Show me one more time . . . I can't quite remember how it was. . . ."

On the verge of losing control, Alanna had no suitable retort. Instead, she gripped his shoulders for support. "I can't," she whispered, knowing that, once she began to give in to him, she would be helpless.

"Sure you can." He spoke with such gentle conviction that she had to listen. For while one part of her fought the incipient cry of desire that murmured through her body, the other part sought a rationale to permit its full and joyful expression.

His hands framed her face, tilting it up toward his as he spoke, his lips but a breath away. The dim light from the nightstand cast his manly features into bold relief, imbuing them with even greater positive force. "Forget who you are, what you are. Forget who I am, what I am." His tone was near-hypnotic; her eyes were glued to his commanding features. "Forget where you were today, where you are now, where you may be tomorrow. All that matters is this moment. Your woman to my man, my man to your woman. Give in, Alanna. Explore the feeling. It's new and wonderful."

His soft words were headier than any wine, his nearness more potent than any drug. With the tremor that passed through her went all thought of resistance, all will to protest. In its place was the taste of passion he had given her and the yearning to know more. Yet Alex awaited her sign. He wouldn't force her, nor would he allow her to remain passive. Intuition told her that he would demand in return everything he gave. The thought excited her. If she wanted him she would have to challenge him as well.

The thought was made all the more exciting by his hands, which drifted from her face to her shoulders, then lightly down her arms to rest expectantly at her hips. "You can't do it," he goaded softly. "Why? Not woman enough?"

The spell was momentarily broken. Alanna gasped at his taunt and its implication, stunned by the maelstrom of emotions that swirled within her. Indignance blunted anger, to be quelled in turn by desire, which erupted in a sigh of need, raw and ever-building. Freed of all pretense by his dare, she would meet him head-on. *He* would eat *his* words, she vowed, by the time she was done.

Her hands lifted to his face, her fingers tracing the rugged lines of his cheek, his jaw, then running around to the vibrant hair at the nape of his neck. His pulse throbbed beneath her thumbs, her own quickening to keep time. When she lifted her lips he met them, still holding back, still demanding that she take the initiative. Unspoken, the dare was repeated. And she met it, deepening her kiss, running the tip of her tongue along the firm line of his lips, then venturing further with darting sweetness in a bid to contest his ability to withstand her provocation. His imminent surrender was electrical.

Slowly he raised his arms, his hands tightening around her, lifting her until she was nearly off her feet. She clung to him for support as his lips grew active, demanding. To her starved senses it was a delightful feeling, that of yielding to a power greater than herself, of absorbing that power and gaining strength from it. With that strength she returned his kiss, weaving her hands through the thickness of his hair to hold him closer.

Her feet left the ground as he lifted her, his kiss as strong as ever while he carried her to the bed. The coolness of the sheets against her flaming body, however, was a stark reminder of reality.

"Alex . . . ?" she whispered, only to be stilled by his thumb against her lips.

"Shhh. I said I'd put you to bed. I'm only doing that."

When his hands reached for the tie of her robe she demurred. "Alex!"

"Shhh. You'll wake everyone up."

His lips silenced her further, drugging her anew as his fingers drew the robe apart, then slid within to begin a sensual exploration of the curves that awaited enticingly. He stroked her sides and her midriff with maddening torment until, caught in an explosion of need, she arched toward him. Only then did he touch her breasts, lightly at first and with a tenderness that hit its mark. This gentleness was totally irresistible. Though his touch grew bolder it was exquisitely precise.

Alanna's palms itched to touch as well. Her gaze followed them as they moved to the vee of his robe, settling against his bronzed chest to allow her fingers access to its hair-roughened warmth. Reveling in this textured landscape, her fingers trailed downward. Muscles rippled beneath her fingertips in a deep tremor of excitement which accompanied his low groan. In the dim light her eyes were bright and alive, her lips moist and open as he reached for them with raw hunger. Then reality entered to shatter their intimacy.

"Are you two at it *again?*"

For a split second they stilled, stunned, tumbling from the heady peak of passion. Alex's subsequent groan was one of frustration as he pushed himself up to rest on stiffened arms.

"Sylvia," he growled huskily, identifying the intruder without even looking around, "you're worse than any chaperone!"

The nurse stepped into the room and closed the door behind her. Mercifully, she didn't approach the bed. Alanna's flush was mirrored on Alex's face, a flush of passion, not embarrassment. Her eyes drank in his color, his hair in disarray, his gaze still dark with desire.

Though stern, Sylvia's voice held an undertone of appreciation. "May I remind you that this is a hospital? We're all here on official business."

It was Alex's discomposure that gave Alanna the strength, despite her lingering exhilaration, to rebound. "That's right, Alex. This is a hospital." She grinned, feeling safer from her own rampant desire with Sylvia in the room. "Official business only. You heard the woman." She felt an odd satisfaction at having the edge on Alex Knight, regardless of how tentative or superficial it might be.

"I hear, I hear," he muttered grudgingly, admitting defeat only for the moment. "You haven't heard the last of me, Ms. Evans." Leaning down, he placed a sober kiss on her cheek in a show of defiance before levering himself off the bed, straightening his robe with dignity and stalking barefooted to the door. "And *you*, Nurse Frazier, had better wipe that smirk off your face. Hmm," he paused, eyeing her closely as Alanna followed the action from her bed, "what happened to the timidity that gave you such tact earlier?"

"That timidity, Mr. Knight," she countered with an utter absence of the quality in question, "vanished with your clothes. As soon as you shed them you became *my* responsibility. As is Ms. Evans. And I will have no hanky-panky in this sleep lab."

Alanna stifled a grin, but Alex was less successful. His head fell back as he chuckled broadly. "Hanky-panky?" He finally caught himself. "This isn't hanky-panky. I plan to marry that woman." One steady hand pointed back toward the bed, then shifted to his hip. "What you interrupted was a lovers' tryst, a meeting of minds and hearts and bodies—"

"Enough, Mr. Knight!" Sylvia threw her hands up in exasperation, then clamped one on Alex's arm and ushered him through the door as though he were a recalcitrant child. "Back to bed."

Though Alanna had been unable to see his face during the exchange she had clearly heard his humor. Annoyed as she was that he should reveal his bizarre whim to a third person, the situation was suddenly funny. Or was it the fact that it was nearly four in the morning and she was strangely light-headed? Or was she light-headed because of Alex's lovemaking? Regardless of the possibilities, the roguish glance he had cast over his shoulder at her just before he disappeared had done nothing to bring her down to earth. Sylvia did, however, returning quickly to—of all things—wire her up again.

"Oh, Sylvia," Alanna opted for sheer honesty, "my mind is humming, my face is flushed, my pulse is racing—and you're really going to record *that* for posterity?"

The nurse was well aware of the predicament, as her knowing mock-glower suggested. "It may be the only way to keep him away from you for the rest of the night." The older woman stopped fussing over her equipment as she reran the earlier conversation in her mind. Her expression was suddenly kind. "Are you two really going to be married?"

Alanna grinned mischievously. "Alex seems to think so. But he's in for a rude awakening. I have no intention of marrying anyone. Not to mention the fact that I only met him for the first time tonight . . . in the cafeteria."

"Oh, dear," Sylvia moaned, "I'm afraid that was my doing. I had no idea he'd make a pest of himself. It's usually the women who pester him!"

Alanna could only muster a pointed "Oh?" before the nurse rushed on. "Of course, it's about time he did settle down. I've known his family for years now. They spend their share of time here in the hospital, what with donating such large amounts of money and all. They keep track of everything that happens here—"

"As though they owned the place?" Alanna couldn't restrain an echo of her earlier statement to Alex, but regretted its sting instantly.

Sylvia, however, didn't seem to mind. "They've been very generous and they happen to be lovely people, every last one of them." Absently she began to reconnect the electrodes.

Alanna saw the opening and she quickly took advantage. "Every last one of them? Just how many Knights are there?" Though the Knight name frequently graced the pages of the local papers Alanna had never followed the family in detail.

The nurse laughed. "You'd sometimes think there

are one thousand and one Knights, what with their presence around this hospital. Let me see," she rolled her eyes, "there are the senior Knights, the junior Knights, and five Knights of your Alex's generation, not to mention a handful of grandchildren, most of them born right here in this hospital."

Alanna ignored the reference to *her* Alex, sighing wistfully. "How nice to be part of a large family. Is Alex the oldest? He said that he heads the foundation."

Sylvia completed her wire-work, placing the last two electrodes on her patient's temples. "I believe he has an older sister or two. He *is* the oldest son; that's why he has taken over the company."

"Is his father ill?" It seemed the logical conclusion, for a father to turn over the running of the family business to such a relatively young son.

"No. Ironically, the money they donate to this place rarely benefits them. They are, as families go, very healthy." She stood back, pensive. "No. But the Knight family works in unique ways. The father hands control down to the son early on, the theory being that in order to benefit from the extensive education they give their children, that up-and-coming blood has to have power. Hence, your Alex is now in charge."

"He's not *my* Alex!" Once, she could ignore; a second time, she could not. But curiosity came fast on the heels of reproach. "Are his parents still . . . active?"

"Hah! You wouldn't be asking that if you had seen them at the dedication of this wing a few months ago.

Alex may be the official head of the foundation, but his parents are very visible indeed! Now," she changed the subject without a blink, "are you comfortable?"

Alanna glanced at the machines beside her. "I suppose so."

"Then good night. Or rather, good morning. I'll be going off duty at six. The daytime nurse will wake you at seven. Think you'll be able to fall asleep?"

"I certainly hope so," she answered quietly. "Much longer and it will be dawn. Then there will be no point in even trying." Her lips thinned in frustration. "And I have to *work* tomorrow. . . ."

Sylvia sensed her frustration. "There, there. Don't get yourself worked up about it or you'll never be able to sleep. Concentrate on relaxing. Try to clear your mind of worry and annoyance." She grinned slyly. "Think of Alex."

Against her will, that was exactly what Alanna did. She found herself conjuring up images of a face that was bronzed and rugged, a body that was warm and firm, a voice that was deep and resonant. She felt her pulse begin to speed up and determinedly focussed on more steadying topics, only to find her mind drifting back once more to lips that were masterful in the thoroughness of their kiss.

She felt those lips against hers as though they were real—then realized, in a moment of shock, that they were. Her eyes flew open to make out the bare outline of his form in the darkness. It was the world of sensation which was fully illumined for her—the warmth of him, the scent of him, the solidity of him beneath the hand she raised.

"Alex?" She whispered hoarsely. *"What are you doing?"*

"Just kissing you goodnight, love." His breath fanned her cheek, then tickled her ear. "I brought your specs back—you left them in the lounge. They're on the dresser now. Sleep well." He kissed her once more, a firm declaration of possession, then was gone.

He was crazy! That's all there was to it! *Crazy!* Creeping back into her room after Sylvia had so deliberately ousted him! *Crazy!* And his weird persistence on the subject of marriage . . . ! *Absolutely crazy!* Then she caught her breath at the realization that, for all she knew, *she* was crazy, *too!* Why else would her body be tingling and a strange sense of comfort be floating about her? Why else would she be touched, as she was now, at the thought that he had been looking after her, even in this very small way? Why else would she be wondering when she would see him again? In the morning? That night? When? Oh, yes, there was certainly a touch of craziness in her, all inspired by one Alex Knight. On that oddly giddy note she fell asleep.

As Sylvia had promised she was awakened at seven by the new nurse on duty, a young, extremely attractive woman about whom Alanna immediately began to wonder. Had she woken up *all* of the sleep lab patients? Of course, she must have. And that would include Alex. Had *he* appreciated that? He seemed the type, she mused snidely, not even bothering to excuse her waspishness as part of her early morning mood. Perhaps Ellen Henderson was right; at this moment Alanna would have liked nothing better than to stroke out her frustration at the swimming pool down the street. With a sigh she began to dress. That would have to wait until tomorrow when she was equipped with her suit, cap and goggles. For today, she had better concentrate on getting herself in shape to function as usual at WallMar Enterprises. She would stop at home after work today for anything she might need tonight and tomorrow.

Dressing carefully in the clean clothes she had packed yesterday, she struggled at length with her makeup to counter the inner tension she felt. When the nurse returned with the coffee she had requested, she was grateful. Coffee helped. Standing back finally to examine the finished product, she was satisfied. Her plum-hued dress hugged her figure and contrasted with the lightness of her coloring. Her hair was pulled back into its traditional sleek knot, exuding efficiency. Her eyes were highlighted with brown, her cheeks accented with pink, her lips glossed with plum to blend with the dress. Glasses perched upon the bridge of her nose, she hoisted her bag, then her purse, and headed for the door.

There was no sign of anyone in the lounge. Passing by the nurses' station, Alanna handed in her log and the half-completed questionnaires, then headed for the cafeteria and some breakfast. Again there were no familiar faces. It was only when she had retrieved her car from the lot and was headed for work that she admitted a twinge of disappointment. Alex must have left even earlier than she had. What did he look like, fresh in the morning? Or did he awaken with a touch of the bear, as she did? Perhaps it was for the best that their paths hadn't crossed, after all. He needed time to realize the absurdity of his proposal—and she needed time to reinforce the same idea in her own mind. The morning light clearly illumined its folly. Alex was headed for his life, she for hers. This was the way it was destined to be; it *was* for the best.

WallMar Enterprises welcomed her, as it did each day, with a deskful of messages and memoranda. Here was involvement—instant and unavoidable. Within the quarter hour she dealt with three men, all unit directors under her jurisdiction, who entered simultaneously, each bent on testing the strength of her shoulders. There was a small matter regarding personnel concerning one of the men, a more critical issue of funding for a newly instituted project concerning another. It was the third, however, who drew most deeply on her store of patience.

"I tried to get you last night, Alanna." It was Brian Winstead who confronted her insolently. "There was no answer at your apartment. I gave up at about one." His tone lowered in scathing sarcasm. "Is your phone out of order?"

Brian's implication was obvious. Alanna's refusal to stoop to his level was equally so.

"I was out all night," she stared boldly at him, challenging him to deepen his slander to her face. With two onlookers, the standoff was a tense one. Whether it was the chill of her glare or the evenness of her words, or simply the fact that she was his superior in the corporate structure, Alanna did not stop to analyze. When he failed to offer a follow-up she continued smoothly, "What seems to be the problem, Brian?"

Sitting behind her desk, the image of composure,

Alanna hid from the world the inner torment that this subtle needling caused. The three men before her stood witness to her utterly professional handling of the problem, a matter of delays in the shipment of several lab supplies, the manufacture of which was a new direction for WallMar, which had earned its reputation as a quality company with a number of paper products. Making notes to herself as Brian spoke, she offered her spontaneous advice, with promises of more specific information later in the day.

After the trio's departure she helped herself to a cup of coffee from the department supply, then returned to her office, shut her door and spent twenty minutes studying the proposal from her next three visitors, who arrived promptly. They were scientists, men with whom she had already met on three separate occasions. The project they presented was risky, but did have the potential, in her eyes, of developing into a lucrative venture for WallMar Enterprises. Alanna eagerly briefed Jake Wallace on the meeting as soon as the scientists had departed.

"It's a fascinating proposition, Jake," she began, taking a seat close by his own desk chair. Her folders were on his desk; as she needed papers from one or the other she reached easily for them. "We've never ventured into this particular field before."

Jake Wallace stroked his clean-shaven jaw. "Umm. Biotechnics. Sounds very complex. Do *you* understand it?"

"Yes. It's really very simple. These men want to be able to apply modern biological techniques to make highly accurate tests for diagnosing various diseases.

What interests us, obviously, is that they need our money. The total amount we're talking about is roughly one percent of our assets, so our risk is a reasonable one. With this money they can put together and—with our help—produce and market kits for diagnosis."

Jake nodded, listening intently as he skimmed the page of figures Alanna had placed before him. His ability to listen and read simultaneously always amazed her, yet he did both well. It was as though his mind was able to soak up information much faster than most; Alanna admired and envied the talent.

She sat back silently as he read the rest of the information she had compiled. When he lifted his head he smiled and she knew she had cleared the first hurdle. "Think you have another winner, Alanna?" The twinkle in his eye hinted at a touch of paternal pride.

"I think *we've* got another one, Jake. I haven't steered you too far wrong yet, have I?"

"Since you've joined us, my dear, you've had miraculous success. If it hadn't been for that small matter of desktop computers—"

Alanna grinned, sensing his teasing. "I'll never live that down, will I?"

"Well, blast it, girl, you keep doing everything else right. It's only fair that you make a mistake or two—and that *we* can know that we're not the only ones who make them. You do know," he sobered abruptly as his train of thought shifted, "that the board meeting is coming up next week? I'm proposing you for Executive Vice-President."

"Executive Vice-President?" Alanna's eyes widened in disbelief. "Jake, isn't that a little too much?"

Jake Wallace let loose one of his famous guffaws. "You're the only one in this corporation who would question his own promotion, and there's no one who would deserve it more."

"I don't know. . . ."

"What don't you know? Jim Callahan is retiring and you've already been doing most of his work for the past few months."

"I know. . . ." She stood to walk around the room. It was ironic; when she should be thoroughly pleased she had reservations. Jake was, fortunately, someone to whom she could talk freely. If the promotion did come through she would present a face of total confidence to the company. Now, however, if there were matters to discuss, she could consider both the pro and the con.

"This is awfully close on the heels of my move to Vice-President for Development. Don't *you* think so, Jake?" She turned to face him.

"That was over a year and a half ago," he reasoned gently. "You earned the position then; now you've earned a chance at this new one." He studied her closely. "What is it that worries you?" When she hesitated he helped her. "The men? They're still at it?"

A sheepish smile crossed her face. "Unfortunately, yes. Brian had a good line this morning." She imitated his drawl. "I tried to get you last night, Alanna. . . ."

"And did you explain where you'd been?" Jake, who knew about the IAT study, asked.

"Of course not!" she snapped. "I don't have to explain myself to Brian or anyone else!"

At her vehement defense her mentor grinned. "I

agree with you. That's precisely why you should accept this promotion to Executive V.P. without hesitation. You've earned it and you do the work. That's all that matters." He frowned. "By the way, how *did* it go last night? Any great insight as to the cause of the problem or a solution to it?"

Alanna shook her head, leaning comfortably against the edge of Jake's credenza. "No. It's very interesting —everything that Ellen Henderson told me about insomnia. And I am hopeful. As for last night, however, I'm afraid I have to chalk it up to experience."

"What do you mean?"

"It was an introductory night. I was—as they put it—'wired up' to establish my sleep pattern. The real work, if you can call it that, begins tonight." Even as she talked her mind had shifted to another topic. "Jake," she heard herself speak right out, "have you ever heard of Alex Knight?"

"Of course I've heard of him. Only someone who is deaf, dumb and blind could not be aware of the Knight family!"

"I guess I put that poorly." She smiled self-consciously, thereby attracting Jake's even more intense scrutiny. "*What* do you know about the man?"

"Why?"

It was a typical Jake Wallace rejoinder, bringing a broader, more relaxed smile to Alanna's face. "I can always count on you, Jake," she shook her head in acknowledgement, "to get right to the point."

"That's how I got where I am, my dear. You should know that by now."

"Oh, I know it very well! You seem to be able to sift out the important questions from the unimportant ones. How do you do that?"

It wasn't the first time she had asked him the question; as in other instances, he humored her. "Instinct, Alanna. You've got it, too. And, I'm still waiting—"

"For what?" Her blond brows met just above her glasses.

"For an answer to *my* question. Why do you want to know about Alexander Knight?"

"He asked me to marry him." She dropped the bomb without a blink.

Jake did blink. Several times. "He *what?*"

Alanna stifled her enjoyment of his surprise. Right about now it *did* sound like an uproarious joke. "Actually, he didn't *ask* me. He *told* me. He told me that I was going to be his wife."

"Now just a minute. Is he on the up-and-up?" There was a paternalism about Jake that warmed Alanna to her core. If only her own father had been like this—concerned, excited, protective. But her own father had been in a world of his own—and her relationship with him was a world away.

"He's repeated it several times. He says that he plans to marry me." She shrugged, as though it were the most normal thing in the world to receive a marriage proposition from a man of the apparent social standing of Alex Knight. "Now I need to know what *you* know about him."

"Rumor in corporate circles has it that the man's a whiz. His daddy was one in his day; this one is supposedly new and better. Have you known him long? You never told me—"

"I don't know him! I just met him last night—at the hospital, if you can believe it! He's terribly arrogant."

"And a very good catch!" Jake's quip caught her off guard.

"Jake, you know how I feel about that. Marriage isn't my thing. I'm very happy with my life the way it is. Jake . . ." her tone was warning, "I don't like the way you're smiling."

Jake was, indeed, smiling broadly now. "Sorry, Alanna, but I really think the idea has potential. The man is about the right age; he's well established and respected and you could use—"

"*I could not!*" Dark brown eyes conveyed her determination. Jake knew it well and opted to take a different tack.

"What was the . . . cause for your meeting, in the first place?"

A few deep breaths settled her somewhat. "He's taking part in the study."

"He has insomnia?"

She chuckled, recalling the moment when she had asked Alex the same question. "Yes. It looks as though we're destined to meet at two in the morning in the lounge. Let me tell you, the nurse there is a terrific watchdog. I really have nothing to be afraid of." Her gay explanation was met by full seriousness on Jake's part.

"We'll just invite the two of you over for dinner one night—"

"No, you won't!" She cringed. "I'm trying to *dis-*

courage the man, not the reverse. He's persistent enough as it is without a formal word of approval from you and Elaine!"

Jake remained sober. "I think you should at least give him a chance. Get to know him. See whether he's serious."

"Oh, he's serious, all right! But, I have no intention of pandering to his whim. I really don't have the time—"

"Nonsense!" His two meaty hands came down forcefully on the desk as he sat suddenly forward. "You can make time for anything you want, Alanna. I've seen you do incredible things since you've been here. Yet you still manage to coach those little girls at the pool and cart my Elaine to the beauty parlor and take courses at the university in the evenings. If you want a little romance you can easily make time for it!"

Alanna would long since have squelched this discussion with anyone else. But Jake was like family. When he spoke it was from the heart, and she listened. Not that that kept her from arguing. . . . "I *don't* want romance, Jake. You don't seem to understand."

"You're right. I don't. You know, I do respect you women nowadays. You've really come a long way. But you've pushed aside certain things, forgotten about others. What about love? A family? Children?"

Alanna shrugged, then sighed deeply. "I suppose I've chosen other goals."

"Must it be one or the other?"

"Now, how can I be—heaven help me—the Executive Vice-President of WallMar Enterprises and have a husband and children at home?" she asked grudgingly.

"Men do it all the time. Why not a woman?"

Silence filled the air for long moments. Alanna had never thought of it quite that way. As a matter of fact, she had never spent much time thinking about the subject of a husband and children at all. No man had ever interested her enough to even spark the consideration.

"Why are you saying all this to me now, Jake?" she asked plaintively. "You've never mentioned it before. Why now? I thought you approved of my . . . lifestyle."

Jake stood and circled the desk to throw an arm about Alanna's shoulder. "We *care* about you. You know that. I've never mentioned it before because . . . you never have. I felt it would be awkward to bring it up. But now I have to be honest. You have a lot to give, Alanna. Look at what you do for Elaine and me, for those kids, for so many of the people you come in contact with. Don't you see—you've found any number of substitutes for the family you don't have. Well," his voice lowered and softened, "maybe you should consider whether you're ready for the real thing."

Alanna snorted. "If it's children I want, I could always—"

"—I'm talking about a man. A husband. Someone to spend the rest of your life with."

"I'm an independent woman, Jake."

He eyed her strangely. "You've already proven that. Now it may be time to prove some other things."

Disturbed, she pulled gently away from his arm and

walked across the room, blond head down, hands clasped in front of her. "Please don't confuse me, Jake. My life is perfect as it is."

Her dear friend sighed. "And that's why you have trouble sleeping at night."

"Honestly!" she exploded, looking toward the heavens for help. "You sound just like *him!*" Suddenly she had had enough. "Look, I've got to get back to work. Can we discuss the biotechnology proposal later?"

Jake's smile was understanding. "Sure thing, Alanna."

"Good." Heading for the door, she kept her eyes downcast. "I'll catch you later."

He caught her arm, staying her for an instant. "Just think," he spoke softly, temptingly, "you could have it all. Executive Vice-President. Alexander Knight. Love. Security. Kids. Think about it."

For a last minute, she stared directly at him. "You, my friend, are as crazy as he is!" And with that she made her most regal exit in total defiance of the doubts that raged within. Jake was both friend and near-family. She respected his opinion and what he had said that morning lingered to haunt her throughout much of the day. By the time the sun had lowered in the sky and she headed for the hospital once more Alanna was in no mood to play games with Alex Knight. Having fixed a light dinner at her apartment, where she picked up clean clothes and the other things she would need for the night and the morning, she went directly to the sleep unit. It was her fondest hope that she would *not* bump horns on this particular evening with that very disturbing man.

At least that was what she told herself as she stepped from the elevator and checked in with Sylvia. And it was what she told herself as she dropped her things off in her room. It was what she still told herself as she sat down for a few moments with Ellen Henderson.

Yet her eye surveyed every room she entered, her pulse raced as she spotted *his* name on Ellen's desk, her skin warmed when she sought refuge in the lounge on the sofa they had shared so very, very early this morning. And, finally, when that deep and now-familiar voice crooned softly by her ear she felt strangely satisfied.

"How're you doing, owl-eyes?"

Chapter Four

*W*ithout turning, she raised her head. Her lips bore a hint of a smile as he leaned toward her to kiss her cheek lightly. It was impossible to deny the physical effect he had on her, the melting of her insides at his nearness, the quickening of her pulse. Yet she steeled herself as best she could and feigned sternness when he circled the sofa to sit beside her.

"I'll have you know, Alexander Knight, that Ellen asked some very pointed questions about my sleep pattern. It seems there were certain irregularities at roughly four this morning . . ."

His "Tell me about it," suggested that she had no need; he already knew.

For the first time Alanna's glance stole to his face, finding an instant reward in the warmth it held. There was an openness about him—an openness free of both craftiness and any ulterior motive. She could almost imagine that he was her most intimate friend and lover—then she caught herself. He was neither. He would be neither. Perhaps it was time he understood that.

"Alex . . ."

"Yeeess . . ." he drawled, his gaze devouring her with frightening ardor.

"Alex, this is absurd! You take this as a joke. What excuse did *you* give to Ellen?"

"I told her," he said simply, "that I planned to marry you. I also told her that, while I intend to continue with this study now that I've begun, I can make no promises to keep my hands off you."

"Alex!" She shook her head in disbelief. "This has to stop! We're here for very serious reasons. I don't know about you, but it took *me* a long time to admit the need for help. Now that I'm here, I want it."

He shrugged. "So what's the problem?"

"The problem," her eyes flashed in reproach, "is the matter of complications. Kisses stolen in the elevator, on the stairs, in the lounge, *in bed* . . . it has to end."

Alex sobered. "I agree with you there."

"Then . . . you'll keep a safe distance . . . ?" Whether her timidity was in part attributable to dismay, even disappointment at such an easy victory, she was too involved to ponder.

"I'll do no such thing." His lips were firm with determination. "*Stealing* kisses has to end. Once you accept my proposal, even agree to wear my ring, we can do it out in the open!"

Alanna was sadly daunted by his persistence. Shaking her head again, she looked away. "What am I going to do with you?" she asked, half to herself.

His voice was deeper, closer. "You can begin by greeting me properly. I haven't seen you since very, very early this morning. I've put in a difficult day at the office—"

"So have I!"

"Then let me show you the kind of comfort *you* need."

Alanna had no time to protest. Strong fingers cupped her chin, tilting it up as his lips descended to meet hers, parting them swiftly, then proceeding to adore them with a sweetness that stole her breath. It was the kind of kiss she would look forward to at the end of a long day, the kind of kiss she would rush home to, the kind of kiss she could return with a similar offer of comfort and ardor. Which she did. Spontaneously. Reflexively. Intuitively. Without a thought in the world beyond the delight of the moment. It was a perfect pairing, an intermeshing of lips and tongues in perfect harmony with each other. When one coaxed, the other responded. When one challenged, the other satisfied. When, at long last, he moved slowly to the side, Alanna felt bereft. Her forehead fell to his shoulder; her breath was ragged. His was no better.

"That was nice," he whispered against her ear, his fingers curving around the back of her neck to gently massage it. At no other point did their bodies touch. "I'd like to come home to that every night," he voiced her own thought. "What do you think?"

Alanna lifted her head, struggling to sort out her thoughts against the powerful distraction of the fingers that had slipped beneath the neckline of her blouse to draw lazy circles on her upper back. "I think," she breathed shallowly, "that there is a definite physical attraction between us. It doesn't necessitate marriage."

His fingers halted their sensual barrage and slowly withdrew. Alex's expression grew suddenly taut, enigmatic emotions sharpening his glare. "It's true, then."

His statement, spoken in a low and somber tone, puzzled her. "What is?"

"Rumor." At her continued confusion, he explained. "Part of my day was spent learning everything I could about Alanna Evans. There was quite a bit, starting with your appointment as Administrative Assistant at WallMar Enterprises seven years ago, covering your promotions to Director of Development, then Vice-President. And I understand that Jim Callahan is about to retire, leaving an even more prime position open . . . should Jake Wallace be inclined to name you to it. A remarkably fast rise."

It was the kind of discussion Alanna might have expected to have with one of her more ambitious colleagues—not with Alexander Knight. These words, coming from him, carried far greater impact. Defiance stiffened her spine, hurt directed her gaze. "What are you implying?"

"I think you know."

"Oh, I know, all right." She confronted him with a confidence born of innocence. "But I wanted to hear *you* say it. It's precisely the kind of thing I've had to listen to for the past few years. I expected it from them. Somehow I didn't from you—though I'm not sure why."

For a fleeting moment he seemed the slightest bit unsure. "Are you denying it?"

"I have nothing to deny." Her voice was even, her head held with pride. Only her clenched hands—always her hands—suggested her torment. "If you want a denial you'll have to make the claim first."

His lips softened, though his eyes remained wary. "Always on the offensive, eh, Alanna?"

"What's the matter?" she taunted him. "Don't have the guts to say it?" She could feel herself beginning to boil. "Is this too public a place to air the dirty laundry? It's all right to kiss here, but not to clear the air?"

"Keep your voice down," he warned. His gray-eyed gaze didn't stray from hers.

Alanna stood up. Though she wasn't quite ready to admit it, Alex's unspoken implication had hurt her more deeply than this particular rumor had ever hurt her before. If this man planned to push her to her limits the challenge was now one of maintaining a self-control that was on the verge of shattering.

"I'll raise my voice when and where I please. When I'm at work there is a certain standard of behavior that is expected from me and I stick to it faithfully. *Here* is another matter. This whole thing—insomnia, you, your persistent talk of marriage—is entirely emotional. If I want to yell, I will."

Breathing hard, she stood several feet from Alex. When he smirked, she recoiled. "At least you're not quite the automaton you'd like people to believe," he observed. "Temper is a very good thing."

"Temper?" she cried, then did lower her voice as she realized the extent to which she was letting him upset her. "You haven't heard anything yet! For starters, I want you to leave me alone." She was trembling now.

"I don't want little kisses here and there. I don't want clandestine visits in the middle of the night. And I don't want your nonsense about me marrying you! What man wants a wife who has no scruples?" As his glance sharpened she repeated herself. "That's right. Isn't that what you didn't have the courage to say just now? *No scruples.* A woman who sleeps her way to the top has *no scruples.* There. That thought should keep you away from me!"

With a last scathing glance she made her escape, fleeing to her room, shutting the door, crossing to the night-dark window and tossing her glasses onto the nearby table to stare into nothingness. She felt as though she had been attacked, assaulted by some unknown force. Why had he said that? Why had he implied what he had? And why had she reacted—overreacted—that way? Yes, it was an emotional issue. In the office she could ignore it. Why couldn't she do so now? If she had wanted a buffer against the lure of Alex Knight this misconception was as good as any. Why, then, did she feel battered? Defeated? Anguished?

"I'm sorry, Alanna." Alex had entered without her knowledge and stood close behind her. When he reached for her she flinched, and he dropped his hand.

"Please leave me alone," she demanded coolly.

"I can't do that. I've hurt you. I won't sleep well until I make up for that hurt."

"Sleep well! Hah! I guess that's the bottom line!"

"Sarcasm doesn't befit you, Alanna."

"Then leave and you won't have to listen to any more."

"Not until we straighten this out."

Alanna wheeled around and started for the call button. "Then I'll just get Sylvia in here—"

"You'll do no such thing," he growled, catching her arms and swinging her around to face him. "This is between you and me. We don't need a referee."

"Are you sure about that?" She scowled at him. "You've just had a taste of my 'temper.' When it really gets going it's an awesome thing!"

He was still for long moments, weighing his alternatives. When his grip loosened she quickly tore her arm away and retreated to the window to stand with her back to him, her arms about herself.

"You know, Alanna, I somehow didn't picture you as having a violent temper. When was the last time you lost it?"

He couldn't have asked a more poignant question. She remembered the moment perfectly. "Roughly ten years ago."

"That's some self-control."

"Not really. I just try to . . . minimize situations where I will be pushed that far."

"Tell me about it."

This time it was a request, and so gently offered that she was helpless to refuse. After long moments she began. "I had been dating this fellow—Shep Harding— through the last two years of college. We were very . . . close. When I decided to go on to graduate school—to get an M.B.A.—he put everything on the line."

Alex's voice came from directly behind her. "Career or him?"

"Exactly."

"So you let him have it?" She heard the smile in his voice and it coaxed her on.

"You could say that. I told him that if it was a warm body he wanted he could pick up another one at the student union. If it was *me* he wanted he'd have to accept me for what I was. I had no desire to be at home all day, waiting for him. I wanted to be out *there*, doing things, using every bit of myself—"

She caught her breath as she realized how he might, if he wanted, interpret her words. As though reading her mind he spoke softly, putting his hands gently on her shoulders. This time she didn't pull away. "I know exactly what you're saying, Alanna. And, believe me, I have no doubts that you've earned everything you've gotten—earned it through work in the office, everything aboveboard."

She cocked her head sideways. "How can you be sure? After all, many women today—"

"You're not *many* women, as you were so quick to tell me more than once last night." The light pressure he exerted was sufficient to turn her. She had to tilt her head back to study his face. Its intensity held her immobile, as his hands slid slowly along her arms. "There may be rumors, Alanna. But you have also built a reputation as being intelligent, on top of every situation, an able negotiator and an honest person. What you told me back there," he cocked his dark head toward the door, "what you showed me in the process, suggests that if you *were* having an affair with Wallace—"

"Jake is married!" she interrupted angrily.

His fingers tightened. "I know that. Let me finish. If you were having an affair with Wallace you would never have been able to keep up that image of coolness in the office." He suddenly grinned. "It seems, love, that you're much more of an emotional creature than your very proper facade would lead one to believe."

Alanna felt the beginnings of that melting sensation, the thawing of her chill beside the hearth of Alex's warm persuasion. "I don't deny being emotional," she offered defensively, "even though I do keep emotions out of the office. I *do* deny ever having used my body to achieve advancement."

"*Corporate* advancement," he corrected softly.

"*Any* kind of advancement."

A dark brow shot up at her insistence. "What *do* you use your body for? Wouldn't you say that pleasure and relaxation and fulfillment are goals worth advancing?"

She eyed him warily. "I don't sleep around. Period."

"Did you sleep with Shep Harding?"

"Yes, I did. I thought I was in love with him. It seemed the most natural thing at the time."

"I'm sure it was. There's only one proper way of expressing that deepest love that two people can feel for each other. I'm not condemning you."

"I should hope not! After all, Alex, are *you* a virgin?"

As he laughed aloud his arms closed about her and pressed her more closely to him. "You know I'm not. And I should think you wouldn't want me to be." His voice lowered dangerously, a sensual quality creeping from it into her body. "I've learned by trial and error. I've made my mistakes on others. Now, for you," he pressed his lips to her brow, "I know just how," then her eyes, "to touch," his hands began an exploration of her back, "and tease," then rose to her shoulders by way of her breasts, "and find every sensitive spot." His thumbs caressed her neck and throat; his lips trailed wildfire across her cheek. Alanna couldn't breathe, his assault was so sensually precise. Her heart thudded loudly, barely muted when covered by his full palm. She could only sigh her content at being touched with such tenderness, could only open her lips to the return of his kiss. Then she realized what she was doing. With the greatest effort she tore her mouth from his and quickly clutched at the first thought to enter her muddled brain.

"Have *you* ever been in love?"

Alex allowed the small distance, studying her indulgently. "Are we still relating this to my virginity, or, uh, lack of it?"

"I wasn't," she continued less shakily, "but since you've raised the issue, it's an interesting one. Did you wait for your first true love?"

Looking ceilingward in supplication, he murmured, "Why do I sense an imminent discussion of double standards . . . ?"

"*Were* you in love?"

"Of course not." His eyes met hers. "I was young and curious. *She* was the one who knew what to do. It was a purely physical thing."

"Have you *ever* been in love?" Alanna persisted.

A gray glimmer heralded his response. "I am now."

"Uh-huh," she humored him. "But *before*. Or, more specifically, why have you never married?"

"I've never been in love before."

This time Alanna's eyes rolled toward the ceiling in a silent plea for patience. "But there must have been a bevy of women over the years. Didn't any tempt you into considering marriage?"

Humor lurked at the corners of Alex's lips. "One or two."

"Oh?" Did she actually feel the tiniest twinge of jealousy? *Impossible.*

"As a matter of fact," he said, deceptively sober, "there were *three* times when I considered it. The first time was with Sharon. She was a childhood friend; our families would have loved it. The second time was with Jill. I was at college then and particularly annoyed at my father about some petty matter. I might have married her just to spite him."

"And the third?" she prodded, curious.

"The third," he sighed, "was a dear friend who found herself in trouble."

"Pregnant?"

"Yes."

Alanna's eyes widened. "Yours?"

"No. I'd never even slept with her."

She was puzzled. "But you would have married her?"

"Yes." Alex answered without hesitation. "I thought enough of her to care that the child had a name, a father and some security."

"What about the biological father?"

He took a breath. "He was in Vietnam . . . never made it back." The sadness in Alex's eyes spoke of his own sense of loss.

Alanna's voice lowered. "I'm sorry." Hesitantly, she sought the end of the story. "And . . . what happened to her?"

Snapping back to the present, he raised strong fingers to lightly caress her face. "She lost the baby. But she's gotten married since. From what I hear she's got four kids now."

Alanna struggled to digest this newly revealed depth of Alex's character as she fought to cope with the resurgence of desire that his restless fingers were creating. Alex sensed her moment of vulnerability and seized on it, kissing her thoroughly, searching out the depths which, at that moment, she was helpless to seal off. He *was* the masterful seducer, having perfected the art over the years. And he had found her weak spot.

His lips devastated her with their exactness, drawing small sighs and a growing response from her own. His kiss held just the right blend of advance and retreat, luring her toward the point of entrapment. And what sweet entrapment it was. Mindlessly she swayed toward it, unable to think of anything but the pleasure of the moment.

Then, from amid the sensual eddy, she discovered another of his consummate skills as he very gently began to undress her. One after the other, with quiet deliberation, he released the buttons of her blouse. In the process his fingers brushed her skin again and again, always departing even before the whispered cry had escaped her passion-swollen lips. She was enthralled and quite happily at his mercy. Finally, with the last button, the silken fabric fell open. His hands slid along her flesh, easily finding the simple catch of her bra.

Alanna's knees trembled. His touch was wonderful, inspiring feelings of femininity she had forced herself to forget for too long. Now, with the force of waters suddenly undammed, these feelings surged forward. Eagerly she met his kiss and arched her body against him. His lips clung to hers as, with both hands, he eased the blouse from her shoulders, discarding it and her bra on the floor. His fingers traveled across her flesh, hungry, insatiable, for long moments. Then, with a moan deep in his throat, he lifted her and put her down on the bed. Taking both her hands in his and pinning them to the sheets by her shoulders, he paused to look at her, his gaze searing its way from her face down her neck to the twin peaks of her breasts, now full and creamy, awaiting his touch. Her breath came in shortened gasps, adding to the temptation of her body.

Alanna thought she would explode. This man had unleashed a flood tide of desire within her; only his possession would salve the growing ache within. But he stilled, almost in awe. His hands released hers, then fell to cup her breasts, holding each as he lowered his head to that soft fullness. One at a time he teased the rosy peaks until each was a tiny pebbled dome quivering for more. When his lips returned to hers she could deny him nothing. Her kiss contained her very soul—for it was there that Alex Knight had found her vulnerability.

"I love you," he whispered, then repeated it louder, more firmly. "I love you."

Her returning whisper was shaky. "You don't love me. You may love my body, or some image of the woman you think you've waited for all these years. But you don't love me. You can't. You don't know me."

Alanna watched as he straightened and reached for his tie, his eyes dark with smoldering passion. "I do love you, Alanna." Hard upon the disposal of his tie went his jacket. She lay still, mesmerized. She knew she should stop him—this was totally improper—yet she wanted to see him as he saw her now. Reaching forward, she set her own fingers to the task of unbuttoning his shirt, gasping as she pushed it aside to reveal his chest, so broad and bronzed and solid. He picked her up then and pulled her against him, their bodies, bare from the waist up, touching with a rapture Alanna could only have imagined. She cried aloud at the beauty of it and clung to him, savoring the strength of him against her breasts, her arms, her torso.

"I love you, Alanna. I need you." He spoke softly and with conviction, his breath wisping the few loose strands of her hair. He held her back and removed each pin in turn, then spread her golden tresses over her shoulders, his fingers going on to trail further over her flesh.

Alanna was caught up in a hurricane of desire. Its winds blew with such force that she couldn't resist it. His words rocked her, yet she couldn't refute them. His hands inflamed her, yet she couldn't pull away. Her senses swirled round and round, faster and faster, each concentric circle bringing her closer to the center of fulfillment.

Nothing was beyond his reach. His lips never left hers for long, drugging her again and again while his hands played against her with the very expertise of which he'd spoken. She was vaguely aware that he had removed her skirt, but it didn't matter; all that was real was the headiness of his touch, the driving need for more of him.

It was Alex's raw whisper that brought her out of her daze for a moment. "Alanna," he growled, "do you know what you're doing?"

Blinking, she followed his gaze to her hands—*her* hands—where they lay at his belt. She knew exactly *what* she was doing; it was the *wisdom* of the move that halted her abruptly.

"Oh, Alex," she moaned in apology. "You do something to my mind! I had completely forgotten where we are—"

He took her hands in his and lifted them to his mouth, kissing her curled fingers. "I think we've both been carried away." His pause was pregnant with meaning, his eyes growing darker by the minute. "Damn it! I can't even say we'll carry on at my place tonight, can I?"

At first Alanna shared his regret. For the first time in years she had wanted a man. Really *wanted* him. Even now her body cried out its need. On second thought, however, she *was* appalled at the setting. This hospital room was no place for lovemaking. And this hospital room would be her home for the next two weeks.

Finally she was relieved. Things had happened much too quickly. To have been carried away by an overwhelming physical craving would have been wrong. She was a woman of calm and careful deliberation, not one to be bowled over by a singularly attractive man. And he was attractive. No, *magnificent*. Her eye skimmed over his physique in appreciation; then she was jarred out of her reverie by his low bark.

"If you continue to look at me that way I won't be responsible for anything I do. So help me," he looked over his shoulder, "I'll make love to you in the bathroom with my back against the door to keep Sylvia out!"

Alanna burst into spontaneous laughter. "That's an amazing picture," she finally gasped, crossing her arms over her chest in a token gesture of propriety. "I don't think Sylvia would appreciate your efforts."

"My efforts, Alanna, are going to be played through in another minute if you don't do something to stem the tide." Standing, he hauled her up beside him, turned her toward the bathroom and gave her a firm but gentle shove. "Take a shower or something. *I* intend to!"

Smiling now from another emotion entirely, she took his advice, seeking haven in the bathroom, stepping out of her slip and panty hose and finally discarding the wisps of silk that were her panties atop the pile. Her thoughts were of Alex as she bent to turn on the water, then stretched to adjust the shower spray. He was, in spite of his arrogance and his one-tracked determination to marry her, an endearing sort. And the effect of his lovemaking on her—that went unchallenged. Standing nude before the mirror, she reached back to wind her hair atop her head when her attention was caught by a movement in the mirror.

"Alex!" She whirled around, then stood stock-still, caught anew in the web of enchantment he cast so well.

His eyes didn't miss an inch of her, yet she stood proud and unwavering before him. When he approached she let her hands fall to his shoulders. His shirt was on but still open. It had taken only his gaze to ignite the sparks of passion, barely banked at best, within her. His nearness now was more than she could bear. If he intended to carry out the threat he'd uttered moments before she wouldn't stop him. Her own need was far too great.

"I love you," he moaned against her lips, kissing her deeply, plunging his tongue into her mouth, tasting every recess before wrenching his lips away. Her fingers were white as they clutched his shoulders, her shudders visible when he bent his head to kiss her neck and tongue her breasts. When he moved lower she could only let her head fall back and sigh her delight. That Alex should take such pleasure in her body was heady enough in itself; that his pleasure should set off such shock waves of ecstasy within her was even headier.

At what point her knees buckled she didn't know. Suddenly she found herself kneeling with him. His hands framed her face; his lips caressed her features. It was only the taste of the moisture on his upper lip that brought a returning glimpse of reality.

"The shower!" she cried, jumping up to fumble with the controls until a deep voice from behind gave a firm order.

"Get in, love. I'll see you later."

She turned in time to see him leave the bathroom and its penetrating cloud of mist.

Hot, hot water punished her body in a steady stream as Alanna tried to understand what had happened. There was Alex—Alex who declared his intent to marry her, Alex who claimed he loved her, Alex who wanted her very much. And there was Alanna—a passionate Alanna she barely recognized. The Alanna she thought she'd known had no need for a man; this one craved Alex desperately. The Alanna she thought she'd known was in full and absolute control of herself; this one had thrown caution to the winds and lost herself in desire. The Alanna she thought she'd known was a professional, with her life neatly mapped out; this one wondered what the future held.

Without doubt she was still opposed to marriage. She had spent the past ten-plus years of her life building defenses against it. Hadn't her mother told her, "Don't succumb, Alanna. You have too much to give. Develop yourself to your full potential. Don't end up *this* way. . . ."

She grasped the shower control and twisted it until the water ran cold and sharp. The frigid battering was just punishment for thoughts of yielding to the autocracy of Alex Knight. If she married him *she* would be a Knight. Her mind conjured up the image of a docile society bride, sweetly accompanying her husband to dinner parties and openings and yachting meets and Labor Day barbecues. What would happen to Alanna Evans? Though poised and polished, she was not of that ilk. She had her own life . . . and liked it that way.

With a muffled groan she turned off the shower. As she dabbed the moisture from her skin her thoughts turned to the phenomenal physical attraction she felt for Alex. It was mutual—and that made it all the more exciting, all the more dangerous. Where would it end?

"Don't be stupid, Alanna," she chided herself aloud. "You know perfectly well where it will end if you don't watch yourself." Her eye moved to the bathroom door. For a moment of reckless imagining she wondered what it would have been like had Alex made love to her here. She pictured his limbs, long and tanned, his hips, narrow and strong. When a tingling erupted in her middle she fought the image, but it persisted. In all the years during which she'd built her career she'd never been attracted to a man this way—and there had been plenty, *plenty*, of men to choose from had she wished. Why Alex? Why now? Why here?

Cautiously, she opened the door, saw that her room was empty and held a towel against herself as she retrieved her nightgown from her bag and slid it over her head. That done she brushed her hair with a fierceness born of frustration, then settled down to tackle the questionnaires and sleep log she had neglected the night before. By eleven-thirty she was asleep.

By two-fifteen, however, she was awake. The room was dark and quiet. She lay on her side, one hand tucked under her pillow, the other comfortably before her on the bed. The pale sliver of light which crept beneath her door was the only source of illumination. It took several moments for her to awaken enough to move, then stretch, then gradually make out shapes in the darkness. She sat up with a gasp.

"It's all right, love." Alex rose in one fluid motion

and crossed to her bed from the chair in which he had been sitting. "It's only me."

"How long have you been here?" she whispered, her perceptions still hazy.

"I'd guess for about half an hour."

"If Sylvia knew . . ." All grogginess had vanished.

"Forget Sylvia." He lifted the covers and slid in beside her before she could anticipate him. "I'm tired, but I can't sleep. Just let me lie here for a while."

It was the sound of true fatigue, the innocent need in his voice, that Alanna found most irresistible. With tentative obedience she let him pull her back against him, curving her body to the firm lines of his. His arm fell across her waist, anchoring her in place.

"Don't you think we're playing with fire, Alex?" she whispered.

"I know we are. But we have no choice. It's either this—or freeze."

His analogy was not quite apt, but she let it go without a fuss. In truth, lying here with him like this was a treat! Then, feeling guilty, she thought back on what Ellen had told her, seeking some justification for this late-night rendezvous.

"What were you thinking when you woke up, Alex?"

"I don't know," he snapped in odd annoyance, then calmed quickly. "I just woke up."

"Right *after* you did, what kept you awake? Normal people simply fall back to sleep once they awaken. We don't. Ellen suggested trying to pinpoint what type of thoughts keep us awake."

"Don't ask."

"I *am* asking." When he remained silent she tried a

different approach, one that appealed to the sense of challenge they shared. "You said you loved me, Alex. If that's true you should feel free to share your thoughts with me. *Do* you love me—or are those simply three empty words?"

She felt his body tense behind her, then relax once more. "You play a mean game, Alanna."

"What were you thinking?" she persisted. "If I'm supposed to help you and in the process help myself, as Ellen suggested, we have to talk."

He pondered her words, stirring for a moment to draw her even closer. "You really want to know?"

"Yes!"

He inhaled deeply of the scented jasmine in her hair, rubbing his cheek against its silken flow before speaking. "I had a dream. It's the same one, over and over and over again, but I can never remember it after I wake. The feeling is always the same though, the feeling it leaves me with."

"What kind of feeling?"

"Emptiness. A pervading sense of emptiness."

Alanna suppressed a shudder. "Is that what kept you awake when you woke up tonight?"

"No." He seemed to hug her more tightly. "This time, when I woke up I thought of you."

"Alex . . ." she warned in a whisper, but he overrode her objection.

"You asked. You'll listen. I thought of you. I pictured you standing in the bathroom the way you were earlier. Your skin, pale and satiny. Your breasts, ripe and full. Your hips, slim and . . . so very ready for me—"

"Alex! No wonder you can't fall asleep! Why do you torment yourself over something you can't finish?"

Somehow Alex sensed her own torment. His voice was suddenly clearer. "Why do you say that?" When she had no ready answer he prodded, "Come on, Alanna. I may be reading between the lines—"

"You're not." She sighed, realizing that she'd fallen into a trap of her own making, one from which only the truth would free her. "I said that because it was the only thing that allowed *me* to fall asleep earlier. Men aren't the only ones with needs, you know."

"I thought you told me that you could do very well without me."

"I said," she corrected softly, "that I had no need for marriage, to you or anyone else."

"Haven't you *ever* considered it?"

"No."

"You've never fancied yourself in love since Harding?"

"I've learned the difference between 'fancying' and 'being.' No, I've never been . . . either . . . since Shep."

"But you do date."

"Once in a while."

"Who?"

"Who what?"

He tugged her closer in mock punishment. "Who do you date?"

Alanna shifted to peer up into his stern face. "Don't get yourself worked up, Alex. They're all just . . . friends."

"*All?*"

"There aren't a whole lot. And I rarely date anyone more than once or twice."

"A policy?"

"No, it just turns out that way."

"Would I know any of your men?"

"They're not 'my men' and I doubt it. They're as far away from the business world as possible."

Alex resettled himself in the darkness, sliding one long leg through hers. "No risk of compromise?"

"None."

"Smart girl."

"Only half of me is smart," Alanna quipped, feeling surprisingly at ease. "The other is selfish. I have no desire to spend an evening out discussing business when I deal with it every hour of the day."

"What *do* you like to do?"

"Oh, I enjoy a fine restaurant now and then, the theater, a movie."

"Parties?"

"A quiet one once in a while. Usually not, though. I like my free time to be more private."

"Ahah! A woman after my own mind! Just me and thee—"

"Alex . . ." Her tone held a gentle warning and his facetious singsong faded. In the next instant she almost wished she'd let him go on with his kidding, for he grew less playful, more pensive.

"A minute ago you spoke of needs, Alanna. Were you serious?"

She hesitated, suddenly fearful of the direction his thoughts were taking. But she couldn't lie. "Unfortunately, yes."

"Why 'unfortunately'?"

Her shrug was cushioned by his chest. "I always liked to believe that I had total control. . . ."

"According to what you've said you haven't been with a man for a very long time."

"I haven't."

"Then why would you suddenly have this problem with *needs*? Why the flare of raw physical desire?"

Alanna flinched at his bluntness. "You put that so delicately," she muttered beneath her breath, but he ignored her subtle rebellion.

"Why, love?" he asked softly. "Why now?" He pondered her silence as she asked herself the same question. But Alex came up with the answer she had hitherto refused to acknowledge. "It's *me,* isn't it?" Again he paused and again there was silence. "Answer me, damn it, Alanna. Am I the first one to stir those feelings since—"

"Yes." Though she whispered the word almost grudgingly, he heard it well. A tremor passed through him in response.

"Ahhhhh," he breathed against her hair. "That's the nicest thing I've heard in years. It almost makes insomnia worthwhile."

Alanna didn't know what to say. Her confession was one she would rather not have made. Would he use this information against her? Would he use her weakness to push her toward marriage? Would he take total and merciless advantage of the physical attraction he now knew she shared?

To her astonishment he did nothing but shift more comfortably behind her. She felt his chest against her back, his thighs against her own. A gentle hand tucked a loose strand of her hair behind an ear, then stroked her cheek lightly.

"Good night, love," he whispered contentedly. Within minutes his slow and steady breathing told of his return to sleep. Alanna had little time to debate the wisdom of his staying, however. Within minutes the warmth of his body and the comfort of his presence put her to sleep as well.

When she awoke the next morning to feel a tentative hand on her shoulder it was that of the day nurse, not Alex. He had, at some prior and unknown point, returned to his room, saving them both a spate of awkward explanations. Indeed, in her morning daze she wondered whether she had imagined the entire episode. It had been lovely and uncomplicated—his crawling into bed to sleep quietly with her. And she could not deny one very notable fact: last night, even given her brief period of wakefulness, she had slept more soundly—and now felt more refreshed—than at any time in recent memory! On that very intriguing note she headed for the swimming pool.

Chapter Five

*W*hen Alanna arrived at the pool, an indoor facility she had had occasion to visit several times with her girls, there were already a dozen early risers swimming laps. She sat on the edge to tuck her hair beneath her cap and position her goggles when something caught her eye. Or rather, someone. A man. He was easily the most proficient of the swimmers. He stroked smoothly from one end of the pool to the other, then flipped underwater to begin the return lap.

Despite her impatience to start her own lap she found her gaze following this man, mesmerized. Powerful arms pulled him forward with every stroke, those same arms glistening beneath the bright lighting as they sliced the air before entering the water again. His motion was unhurried, his breathing steady. His legs scissored only enough to ensure a streamlined stroke.

"Are you going?" The voice of another swimmer waiting for his own turn to enter the water brought her from her trance.

"Thank you, yes." Lowering her goggles, she slid into the pool and smoothly kicked off from the side.

Lap after lap, she tallied them in her mind. If she made her girls swim half miles each week, she should surely be able to do a mile herself each morning. Forty minutes of swimming. One lap blended into the next as she lost count and the clock remained as the only source of reference.

As she stroked her thoughts returned to that man. He was beautiful. Even now, as he passed her in the opposite direction, overtaking her every fifth or sixth lap and surging ahead with that same steadiness she had admired from the deck, she watched him. How like Alex he was built!

As she began a new lap she conjured up a picture of Alex without his shirt, as he had been for such a short but devastating time on her bed last night. His chest had been broad, like this other man's; the muscles of his arms flexed similarly. Perhaps it *was* Alex! Was it such an improbable coincidence? The coloring was the same—an even sheen of bronze, hair made darker by the water. The height and build were identical, even given the distortion of her goggles. Could it be Alex?

Thirty minutes—and she continued to swim, pacing herself to avoid exhaustion. Several other swimmers had left the pool; several newcomers had joined the group. The man—that man—continued to swim, smoothly, easily, exerting so little effort that Alanna found herself envious. She also found herself surprisingly relaxed when finally, at the end of the mile, she pulled herself from the pool and headed for the showers. From there it was a simple matter of dressing, applying makeup, brushing her hair back and securing it firmly at her nape. When she emerged into the sunshine of a new day she felt more eager for work than she had in months. The tall, lean figure, smartly outfitted in a gray three-piece suit who sat perched on the edge of the low concrete wall, however, jolted her out of her sense of calm. It *had been* Alex! He was now freshly shaved; his hair, still damp, was neatly combed. In his hand was the sport bag that must have contained his own things. With a convulsive swallow she took in his striking appearance and, chin tilted in a semblance of composure, approached him.

"Not bad." He checked the wide gold band of a watch that ringed his wrist. "Most women take—" He mustered a grin. "Forget I said that. Have you had breakfast?"

"No." Her answer was short and breathy; she hoped he would attribute it to haste.

"Then let's go. I think we can pass up the hospital cafeteria this morning in favor of something a little more . . . elegant."

"I really don't eat much—"

"Don't argue with me in the morning, owl-eyes," he growled, leading her by the hand toward the sleek gray Porsche that sat waiting at the curb. "I need time to wake up."

"Didn't swimming wake you?"

"Physically, yes. Mentally, not quite."

"How far did you go?"

"Two miles."

"You must have been up at dawn!"

He opened the door, then stood back to allow her to slide in. His darkened gaze spoke the accusatory volumes that his tongue was not yet quite up to. "Almost."

Breakfast was served on white linen tablecloths covered with the finest of china, silver and crystal at a private club where Alex was a member. It was not until after the first full cup of strong, black coffee had warmed him that he was able to speak in sentences once more. In truth, Alanna found his early morning gruffness appealing; she was not usually up to much herself at that hour.

His compliment came on the heels of fresh grapefruit and startled her. "You're a very good swimmer. I understand you coach?"

"Uh-huh." She sipped her juice. "You're not bad, yourself. You didn't say that you were a swimmer."

"You didn't ask." The twinkling in his eyes softened his tone.

"Your stroke is beautiful," she burst out spontaneously, then promptly wished she had chosen a different word. This one had a poignant double meaning.

"Felt good, did it?" he drawled softly.

With calm deliberation Alanna spread raspberry jam on her English muffin. "That doesn't even deserve an answer."

"What's on the agenda for today?" He startled her with his abrupt change of subject. His obvious interest, however, soothed her ruffled feathers.

"Oh, a pretty full day. I have to go over the cost

sheets on our newest insulation proposal. That should take up most of the morning."

"Is this another of your pet projects?"

She blushed. "So you've heard of them?"

"They're part of your reputation, love. You should be proud of what you've started."

"I am." She spoke softly, taking time out for a bite of bacon. "When I first came to WallMar Enterprises it was strictly a manufacturer of paper goods."

"*High quality* paper goods," Alex interjected, "and handling the largest volume of any such company on the East Coast."

"Did you learn that yesterday?"

"No. I've known that all along. Business is my field, too. Although the Knight Corporation hasn't had any direct dealings with Wallace we're well aware of his achievements. You, love, have gilded the image."

"You sound as though I've done something single-handedly," she protested modestly.

"Haven't you? Jake Wallace may be a whiz, but most of the men beneath him are far from genius material."

"Hmmm, you can say that again. Ah—strike that! It was very improper of me to bad-mouth my fellow employees."

His voice lowered. "Even though they bad-mouth you?"

Alanna nearly choked on her coffee. She put down the cup with a thud, then silently sought to calm herself. "I try to ignore that."

"Perhaps you shouldn't."

She looked up at him, aghast. "What would you like

me to do? Bring them to court for libel? Smear Jake's name and marriage all over the pages of some scandal sheet just to show that I'm innocent of their charges? I'm not even sure I could do that! People will believe what they want. A person may be innocent until proven guilty, but, once heard, a rumor has this nasty way of tainting things, nonetheless."

"What does Wallace say about it?" He sat forward, his eyes alert.

"Jake takes the same view I do. The bottom line is the business. If it thrives and we continue to be effective we try to avoid a confrontation. As a matter of fact, when I told Jake that I doubted whether I should be named Executive Vice-President, precisely because of the rumormongers, who would be bound to have a field day, he disagreed completely. Poor Jake, he *does* see me as one of the family."

"And you?"

Alanna's brown-eyed gaze beamed straight toward Alex. "I love Jake and Elaine as I might have loved my parents. They've been wonderful to me. I only hope that I deserve the faith Jake has shown in me. He gave me carte blanche from the start. From my very first suggestion—the one that led to our entrance into computer software—he's been behind me."

"It was a brilliant move."

"Not brilliant. Simply . . . timely. When I first interviewed with Jake I sensed his willingness to branch out. The projects I head are ventures that risk a small, very small, percentage of our assets. I've had a fair success ratio, thank goodness!"

Alex continued to look at her, his chin resting on one large palm. He seemed content just to sit, moving only slightly when a black-vested waiter refilled their coffee cups. When it occurred to Alanna that she had been doing most of the talking she attempted to remedy the situation.

"How about you, Alex? What are *you* up to today?"

"I've got a meeting in New York at eleven." He sounded totally unconcerned with the matter, despite the fact that time was passing.

"Eleven! And here you're sitting with me! Shouldn't you get going?"

"There's no rush." His eyes beamed lazily. "I'll be flying, anyway. I don't have to be at the airport for a while yet."

Alanna nodded, her gaze clinging to his. Should she ask? Would he be resentful? Wasn't it as good a test as any to see if he really meant to make her a part of his life? "Is it a critical meeting?" She finally opted for indirectness, opening a subject that he could easily close with a "yes" or a "no" should he so desire. To her pleasure, he did neither.

"It's a meeting with the Board of Directors of InterContinental Communications. We've been working to establish competitive sources of long-distance communications; they may be our key."

A vague memory stirred. "Did I read something about that not long ago?"

"You may have, if you're up to date with the trade journals. We've been trying our best to keep it under cover. Unfortunately, the noble people of the press—

whatever press—have ways of sniffing things out." Alanna smiled her understanding. "All done?" he asked politely.

"Yes, thank you. That was good. My breakfasts aren't usually as formal."

He moved to stand behind her to pull out her chair. "See if it helps with the morning. If it does, it may be worth repeating!" His words were low and spoken by her ear; she recalled them often throughout the day.

Indeed, she thought often of Alex throughout the day—far too often for her peace of mind. She thought of how he had been last evening: alarmingly virile. She thought of how he had been in the wee hours of the night: quietly comforting. She thought of how he had looked swimming in the pool: disturbingly masculine. She thought of how he'd been at breakfast: companionable, despite the hour. As the day slowly passed and she went from one meeting to another, from one phone call to another, from one project to another, she wondered what he would be like tonight.

"Alanna!" Jake called from the door of her office, then entered. "Where have you been?"

Her eyes widened. "Right here, Jake. For the past—"

"I know that. I meant your mind. I called your name three times just now before you finally looked up." His gaze was uncomfortably knowing. "Off daydreaming somewhere?"

Alanna couldn't stem the flush of embarrassment that crept upward from her neck. "I guess so."

"How did it go last night?" He honed in on her thoughts.

"Fine. I slept pretty well . . . for an insomniac."

"Do you think the program will help, then?"

She frowned. "I'm not sure." There were now so many complicating factors. "I hope so."

"Have a few minutes to talk about that biotechnics proposal?"

"Sure, Jake." It was a merciful out, a propitious escape. With Jake here and a concrete issue before her it was possible—if only for a short time—to exorcise the ghost of Alexander Knight. No, not a ghost. A ghost implied a relationship from the past. This was more like a glimpse of the future. And that thought disturbed her even more. Her current problem was much like the self-perpetuating wakefulness of the insomniac. The more Alex Knight intruded on her thoughts, the more unsettling he became and the more she found herself engaged in slow brooding on him and on the future.

The day went on much as the one before. As the afternoon passed she grew increasingly apprehensive and Alex bore the brunt of her frustration. By six o'clock she had blamed him for everything from a broken copy machine to a misaligned finance sheet, not to mention the frequent daydreams that took her from her work. As on the evening before, she arrived at the clinic prepared for battle.

It was shortly before nine when she arrived and there was no sign of Alex. The lounge was empty. Ellen Henderson, however, was free and available; they spent some time together reviewing Alanna's sleep charts and discussing her log. Ellen asked general questions relating to Alanna's initial reaction to the program; Alanna answered each as honestly as she could, though she couldn't quite bring herself to mention Alex's name. There were, indeed, several awkward silences during which Alanna suspected that Ellen considered broaching the subject before yielding the initiative to Alanna, who said nothing. For the time being, she was grateful for the reprieve.

By the time she returned to her room it was nine-forty-five and the lounge, which she'd passed through en route, was still empty. Had he come yet? Where was he? Paperback in hand, she returned to the lounge and read—or attempted to read—for another hour. Had something happened to him? Was he all right? The other two members of the study had drifted through; now one approached and sat down. She was a pleasant enough woman, middle-aged and in the upper echelon of an insurance company. She spoke freely of the petty aggravations she'd had to face that day, of the added aggravation she'd have to face when she awoke in the middle of the night, of the doubts she had of the success of this program, and of anything else that came into her head. It was all Alanna could do to sit still.

There had been, still, no sign of Alex. As politely as possible Alanna excused herself and headed for her room. A shower and one hundred brush strokes later she sat propped in her chair, eying her watch. Eleven-thirty. What was keeping him? Had he been held up in New York? Had some evening meeting kept him? Was he—she gasped—on a date?

Eleven-thirty-five. Eleven-forty. Eleven-forty-five. As the time ticked on she pondered her own absurd state. When she'd first arrived at the clinic this evening, a good-sized chip on her shoulder, she had been marginally relieved that he hadn't been there. As the time wore on she had grown upset, then worried. Now her annoyance was directed at herself for her folly. What was the matter with her? Alex Knight was a man whom she'd met barely two days ago. Granted, what they'd shared in the meantime had had its intimate and very personal moments. But the fact remained that they were still free and separate individuals. Alex had no more need to check in with her than she had to report back to him.

On that defiant thought she climbed into bed. Midnight. What had happened to that "early curfew" to which Ellen Henderson had referred? Did it apply to everyone but Alex Knight? Closing her eyes, she willed anger into abeyance and concentrated on nothing. Cool, clear nothing. Nothing . . . disturbed by the dark and handsome image of one Alex Knight. Nothing . . . hampered by worry that something might have happened to him. Nothing . . . marred by the fear that he might, for some unknown reason, have opted out of the IAT study. Despite the turmoil the man engendered within her, she *was* fearful of never seeing him again. Without stopping to consider her feelings more deeply, she hopped out of bed, drew on her robe, opened the door enough to see a clear way to his room and made a beeline for it, pausing on the threshold to still her thudding heart. Her intention was simply to see if he had come in during the past hour. Slowly and stealthily, she opened the door a crack. If he *was* there she would retrace her steps immediately.

The room was dark; no sound came from within. A slice of light from the hall angled across the bed and she opened the door further. There was still no sound. Yet there was a definite human shape on the bed, *in* the bed. Her gaze followed the outline of his body from his feet up, crossing the line where blanket ended and skin began, continuing over his chest to his face.

One long arm was thrown across his eyes, yet his voice was clear. "Aren't you going to come in?"

Caught in the act, Alanna was not sure just what to do. While one part of her wanted simply to excuse herself and run the other was still curious as to why, given his previous attentiveness, Alex had avoided her tonight. The latter impulse won. Slipping through the doorway, she closed the door behind her and hesitantly approached the bed.

"Well?" He sounded neither pleased nor angry, simply tired.

"I just wondered whether you got in all right. I didn't see you earlier."

"It was late; I arrived a little while ago. I thought you might be asleep and I didn't want to wake you."

"You don't need to explain. . . ." she began, feeling guilty at having disturbed him, still wondering whether she should leave at once. As he had in the past, he read her mind.

"Come sit with me, Alanna," he offered in soft invitation. "I could use the company." His arm lifted from his eyes; his hand patted the bed beside him. Without a second thought she found herself there, concerned at his state of fatigue.

"Was it such a bad day?" she asked in a whisper.

The light from beneath the door was too dim to allow him to make out her features; rather, his fingers traced the lines of her face in greeting. "Everything went well in New York, if that's what you mean."

"What happened afterward?"

"Just a small family matter. You know how that kind of thing can eat at you."

"I don't," she contradicted him gently. "I have no family. You're the one who is privileged . . ."

His fingers touched her lips. "I sometimes wonder." When his other hand met the first to cup her face and bring it down toward his she put a hand on his chest for support and eagerly met his kiss. His lips were gentle, tired yet sweet; he seemed to take his strength from her, gaining vibrancy with each moist taste.

It was as though Alanna had waited for this all day. Any anger she had felt earlier simply dissolved. There was only Alex and his warm, strong body. When his kiss ended with a light touch to her nose she moved on impulse to join him in bed, much as he had done earlier. With feline grace she stretched out beside him, finding a comfortable niche for her head on his shoulder, her legs falling easily by and between his. When her hand slid to his waist and hip, however, she jumped and made to retreat. Only his arm held her still.

Her whisper was hoarse with dismay. "Alex! You've got nothing on!"

"I always sleep this way," he countered with nonchalance.

"But this is a hospital—"

"And Ellen said to sleep in whatever we were accustomed to. I'm doing just that!"

"I don't know." Her wariness persisted. "Maybe I should go back to my own bed."

"Don't you dare. I like you right here," his hand curved to her hip, "by my side."

She was more than by his side. She was practically molded to him; their bodies fit that closely together. Desperate to break the aura of sensuality, Alanna cleared her throat and tipped her head back to study his dimly lit features. "What's the problem in your family? Anything you'd like to discuss?"

Just as this morning she had wondered whether he would freely share information regarding his work, so now she wondered just how much he would trust her with something so personal. As earlier, she was warmed by his open and honest response.

"It's my father. He's having some trouble adjusting to retirement."

"How old is he?"

"Sixty-three. He turned the company over to me four years ago, shortly before his sixtieth birthday."

"What has he been doing since then?"

"He and my mother travel a lot, visiting their various grandchildren. They've also taken several extended trips—the most recent one to China.

"But your father isn't comfortable?"

"He's torn. He firmly believes that I should hold the reins of the foundation, yet he can't quite let go completely. It can be . . . very difficult. . . ."

"In what way?"

"Second-guessing. Backseat driving. Monday morning quarterbacking. Should I go on?"

Alanna smiled against his chest, absently rubbing her cheek against the fine hazing of hair there. "I think I understand. Why don't you put him to work?"

"That's what I've suggested."

"Well . . . what's the problem?"

"The problem, love, is his determination to be retired. It's either all or nothing with him. He can't see things quite as clearly as we do and therefore can't see that he's already got several fingers irrevocably in the pie."

"Can't you give him his own division? Something that really needs *his* expertise and experience behind it?"

Alex was quiet for several moments. "You phrase it very well, Alanna. From me, it sounds like a consolation prize. From you, it's an opportunity that demands skill." Again he was silent, pensive, and she was satisfied merely to listen to the steady thump of his heart. His arm tightened around her before he spoke again. "I'll have to remember that—'his expertise and experience.' That might convince him. Better still," he angled his head down toward her face, "you'll come and have dinner with us one night. You can tell him to his face exactly how much the company needs him."

"Oh, no, I won't, Alex Knight. He's *your* father."

"You'd like him—*and* my mother," he crooned invitingly.

But Alanna was determined to stay clear of that powerful trap and refused to even consider the question with any degree of seriousness. "I'm sure I would," she quipped lightly. "But it would be totally impertinent of me to walk in and tell your father what to do. I'm no Knight—"

"—not yet."

"Alex . . . !" Her protest was silenced by the lips which captured hers in their sensual net. Suddenly protest was nonexistent. In a moment of accumulated desire—desire built up through an evening of worry and brought to a head by their present intimacy—Alanna was transported to a world encompassing only Alexander Knight.

In the delirium of his kiss she *was* a Knight, with every right to the luxuries he offered. His lips drank in her goodness in turn; his tongue set off explosive charges deep within her mouth. His legs moved against hers with electrifying friction, binding her to his body. He was fit and solid beside her, beneath her.

"Alex!" She tried again, gasping against his cheek. "This has to stop!" Even her whisper was hoarse.

"Why?" He smoothed her hair from her face and held it back with both hands.

"It's . . . dangerous. You know where we are. . . ."

A faint flicker of white broke through the darkness when he grinned. "We're in bed."

"We're in a hospital room!" she countered, trying desperately to ignore the span of lean stomach spread beneath her palm. When she tried to push against it and lever herself away Alex held her closer. His hands slid down, one to her back, one to her hips, to press her more fully against him. Her protest was aimed as much at herself as it was at him. "I'd better leave, Alex. This is getting out of hand."

"To the contrary." He squeezed her gently. "It's very well *in* hand."

"Alex! This is absurd—"

"And lovely." He moved ever so slightly against her, sending ripples of excitement tingling through her extremities.

"Oh . . ." she exhaled, feeling herself losing touch with reality. "Why do you do this to me?"

"We're made for each other, love. Don't you see that? Why must you fight it so?" His hands held her and molded her, doing wicked things in utter innocence.

"I don't know," she murmured, closing her eyes as his lips planted light, dreamy kisses all over her face. "I don't know." The pleasure was exquisite. What *was* there to fight?

"Let yourself go. Trust me. Let me pleasure you."

With a soft moan of surrender she turned her mouth to his and welcomed the full force of his kiss as it spread the flame of desire to every last pocket of her resistance. Her immediate future was in his hands, yet he worshipped her as though she held the reins.

Alanna's body was aflame, Alex's was its fuel. Her survival seemingly depended on him and she arched toward him eagerly. The feel of his body intoxicated her. She combed her hands across his chest, exploring its every sinew. Its manly hardness pleasured her fingertips beyond description, luring her palms hungrily over him. At her touch he sucked in the taut muscles of his stomach, offering a lean plane for her hands to glide across.

His deft fingers released the tie of her robe, slipped it from her slender shoulders and pulled it from beneath her. As she lay on her back he hovered over her, balancing himself on one elbow, visually caressing her. She caught her breath when his fingers slid the strap of her nightgown from her shoulder, pulling it down enough to free a swollen breast from its silken confines. Within seconds his mouth had encompassed a rosy nipple, gently sucking, sending passion racing through the warmest depths of her body. She cried aloud at the feeling, then cried again when his tongue and teeth played at her nipple, toying it into a hard, dark peak.

Alanna was swept up in a torrent of desire. She was utterly lost in his kiss and the yearning to return its intensity. In a fleeting moment of recollection she knew where she was, but it no longer mattered. All that mattered was Alex and what he was doing to her, what they were about to do together. It seemed the highest point of her life, that moment for which she had waited long, long years alone, compensating for that aloneness with her work.

Again her hands sought him out. He gasped when she touched him, then pulled her over onto him and reached for her face. He kissed her thoroughly, savoring her mouth, adoring its welcome. His hands moved to her shoulders, skimmed the length of her arms, found her hips and slowly drew the soft fabric of her gown up to her waist.

Consumed from within by a burning need, Alanna strained toward him. She wanted him—oh, how she wanted him. Yet she was frightened. It had been so long since she had opened herself to a man. The heat of Alex's body spoke of his own raging fire. He encouraged her with the proof of her power over him. Her breasts brushed electrically against his chest when she bent forward to seek his strength.

"Alex . . ."

"Shhh." He kissed her again, drugging her to near-mindlessness.

"But Alex . . ." The last shred of reason found timid voice. "Here?"

"I need you, love," he rasped urgently. "I need you now." His hands reached for her, but she resisted for a last, frantic moment.

"I'm frightened," she whispered. "I want to please you. . . ."

Her words brought a deep groan of desire from his throat. In one lithe move he rolled her beneath him, pausing only long enough to slip her gown over her head, then feel her nakedness with his restless palms. "You please me already, Alanna. Be mine. I do love you."

At that heady declaration Alanna released any threads of caution. Words became a thing of the past, yielding to a kiss that worked its way over her body, finding tiny pockets of sensuality and bringing them to life. His fingers worked a magic of their own, tuning her to him until she had no separate identity. He led her high with his touch to a peak of clamoring need.

The moment was imminent. Alanna's breath hung in her throat, to be released in a soft, sweet cry when she was at long last complete. Alex had made her so. He must have felt it, too, for he clasped her to him, crushing her breasts against the warm wall of his chest for a long, still time of quiet pleasure.

Then, between murmured heart-words and avid cries

of ecstasy, he made love to her. Slowly, at first, he set the rhythm, drawing her into it faster and with rising hunger. Alanna floated in a world of passion and promise. Her body throbbed with desire in the growing need for fulfillment. Willingly, she let Alex stoke her fires, returning the heat, hotter and hotter until, at last, clutching him, she felt his explosion and knew of her own.

It was a honeyed warmth that spread through her to him and back as they lay, locked tightly together, savoring the last moments of rapture. Alanna felt fulfilled in a way she had never felt before. Her breathlessness echoed his, but gradually slowed as time put its inevitable wedge between glory and reality.

What came over Alanna then, she would never know. With the speed of lightning, her life passed before her, its kaleidoscopic frames suddenly encapsulated in one moment that held more meaning than all the rest.

Helplessly, she began to cry. Tears streamed down her cheeks to dampen his chest as he slid to her side and shifted her in his arms.

"What is it, love?" he whispered, stroking her hair back from her face. "Did I hurt you?"

She could only shake her head against him, choked by the silent sobs that racked her body. Alex's love had released the emotional flood that had been dammed for years, years in which she had neither cried nor sought refuge in arms such as these that now held her so very tenderly.

He let her cry, sensing her need to express feelings so long bottled up. Cradling her gently, he rocked her until the inner storm exhausted itself. Then, his body protectively curved to hers, he pulled the covers over them.

They could have been in their own private bungalow on a deserted stretch of beach in the bright warmth of the Caribbean, honeymooning with abandon, so deep was the relaxation Alanna felt when the silence of the cool northern night enveloped them. In Alex's arms, content and fulfilled, she fell into a deep sleep. Within moments he had followed her. When they awoke it was morning and their bodies were still entwined. To their instant delight was added a note of astonishment: Sated by love and held by each other, they had slept, undisturbed and at peace, through the night.

Chapter Six

*E*llen Henderson was neither delighted nor undisturbed, and peaceful was the last word to describe her expression when she summoned them both to her office early that evening. Alanna took a seat by the desk; Alex perched on the edge of a low file cabinet.

"How *could* you, Alex?" the psychologist burst out as soon as the door was closed. "This is a hospital, for heaven's sake!"

Alanna had already spent most of her day pondering the matter. Neither guilt nor regret had a place among the many emotions she felt. She was confused, perhaps, as to where the future would lead. She was certainly overwhelmed by the effect this one man had on her. She was even a bit frightened of the force of her own response. But she was also pleased and satisfied, strangely at ease with the knowledge of what had occurred so spontaneously last night.

Alex, to whom Ellen seemed content to direct her initial tirade, was likewise free of guilt. He was downright unremorseful. "I'm well aware of what this institution is, Ellen," he answered her smoothly. "But worse things than love have happened at hospitals."

"I'm not talking about *love* and you know it. I'm talking about *lovemaking*. I would have expected a bit more propriety from you, of all people."

Still Alex was totally in control. "Come off it, Ellen. I'm human. I told you I loved her. Don't be a prude."

Ellen bristled. "Tell *that* to the poor little nurse who walked in on you two this morning. *She* was not terribly pleased."

Alanna looked down and pressed a fist against her mouth, yet her soft laugh could not be entirely muffled. Guilty only at finding humor in what so clearly disturbed Ellen, she shot a helpless glance at Alex. His expression mirrored hers, though he managed to refrain from an open show of amusement.

"Poor girl. Did we shock her that much? You know, Ellen, you really should teach your nurses the facts of life."

"Alex . . ." Ellen warned him softly, yet there was an easing of her tension. Now her gaze shifted to include Alanna. "What am I going to do with you?" She threw her hands up in exasperation, then joined Alanna and Alex in spontaneous laughter. "You know, if I weren't a happily married woman myself I'd probably be jealous of you, Alanna."

For the first time Alanna spoke. "I didn't realize you were married. You don't wear a ring—"

"—or use my husband's name or call myself *Mrs.* It may be a modern marriage, but it's worked well for the last seven years, so it's got to have something going for it."

"What does he do—your husband?" Alanna asked, fascinated that a woman with such heavy career demands could successfully manipulate the mechanics of a marriage.

"He's an anesthesiologist here at the hospital. We coordinate our schedules very comfortably."

"How *is* Sandy? I haven't seen him in a long time," Alex asked, obviously as familiar with her husband as he was with Ellen. Alanna turned her attention to his dark, casually posed figure as he proceeded to chat easily with Ellen for several moments.

Despite her outward attentiveness, Alanna's mind wandered helplessly. What *had* last night meant? She felt different, somehow, yet her body was certainly unaltered. It was all within—this difference. In the process of his lovemaking Alex had broken down her defenses. He had breached her emotional guard. She was suddenly unsure of the future, of what she wanted from her life. And she was acutely aware of things she'd never known. Only Alex's presence had made her see her past as one of loneliness. Only his love had rendered all else empty. Where was she to go now?

"The way I see it," Ellen's evaluation broke into her thoughts, drawing her startled gaze, "we have two options, neither of which is totally satisfactory. First, you could continue as part of the IAT study, with strict promises," she looked sharply from one to the other, "to keep your hands off one another. Even if you agreed, I'd be compromising the project by adding a tension that wasn't there before. The second possibility," she sighed, "is for you both to drop out. I have others I can put in in your place."

"What if we got married?" It was Alex's deep voice that posed a third possibility.

Alanna promptly vetoed it. "No!" The force of her refusal brought her to her feet. Suddenly distraught, she looked from Alex to Ellen and back, then walked to the far side of the office to stand with her back to them, her arms wrapped protectively about herself. She felt their eyes on her, sensed when they looked at each other in silent communication. It was Ellen who came to her rescue, rising from her desk to approach and put a gentle arm about her shoulders.

"Look, I have a suggestion," the psychologist began. "We'll chalk this night up to an unavoidable complication. Why don't you both take the time to talk, to decide things between yourselves? I've listed the possibilities relating to the study. *You* have to list the possibilities relating to your relationship. Take tonight off and tomorrow you can let me know what you've decided—whether you want to stay in the program under my conditions."

In the silence that followed Alanna knew that Ellen Henderson's suggestion was fair. The problem of insomnia had taken a definite backseat to this more immediate matter between Alex and herself. At her nod of agreement, Alex spoke up.

"Thanks, Ellen. You've been more than understanding."

"It's my job," the woman quipped with a smile, turning. "But promise me that you'll follow the guidelines I've given you—no liquor or coffee, try to leave the tension behind when you go to bed—" She caught herself up short and an impish smile lit her face. "As a

127

matter of fact, I understand you two did very well last night. No waking up at all?" Alex grinned broadly as he shook his head. "You know," she went on, "I really should be furious." But she wasn't. "You've proven something that I don't even have the guts to commit to paper for fear they'll close down the sleep lab! It would be an interesting proposition. . . ." Her gaze narrowed in feigned concentration.

"It *is* an interesting proposition," Alex spoke for Alanna's ears alone when, several moments later, they headed for the elevator. She couldn't muster any response, but simply remained silent, caught up in the whirl of emotions that stirred within. Alex snagged her gaze for a long enough moment to read her turmoil, then he turned her gently toward him. "We do have to talk. Let's go to my place. I can drive you back to pick up your car later."

She found encouragement in his seeming patience and nodded. The Porsche was in the lot. With a light hand at her back he guided her toward it, then held the door while she made herself comfortable. It wasn't difficult in a car as elegant as this. Conversation was a far more trying matter, however. Alanna didn't say a word. Her thoughts raced wildly in a desperate bid to escape the crux of the issue: *What did she feel for Alex Knight?*

In his arrogant way he had found a niche under her skin. His presence permeated her life with its aura of specialness. How had she let it happen? *Why* had she let it happen? Could it be that she *needed* him?

Defensively, she concentrated on the Alanna Evans who had existed so successfully, all alone, for the past ten years. Her mind dwelt on the image of that self-sufficiency, of professionalism, and by the time Alex pulled up before a tall, modern apartment building in a newly converted area of downtown Baltimore she felt more composed than she had all evening.

"This is home?" She leaned forward to eye the imposing structure.

"Uh-huh." He switched off the ignition and scanned the entrance for a sign of the doorman. "It's comfortable and convenient. When I want to stretch my legs and breathe deeply of country air I drive down to my parents' house."

"Do they live far?"

"It's not quite a fifty-minute drive."

"Do you see them often?"

"I try to get down there once a week. Occasionally they drive up to join me for dinner."

"And your brothers and sisters—" Her voice broke when the doorman unexpectedly appeared to open her door, startling her. Conversation resumed in the elevator.

"I have three sisters and a brother. Joey manages the West Coast office. We talk on the phone often, but don't see each other as much as we would like. The girls are scattered; two are married and one is still in graduate school. She's the baby. She's training to be a pediatrician." His pride was unmistakable.

Alanna was instantly appreciative. "Whew! That's quite a goal!" The elevator opened and Alex led her to a door at the far end of a long, ecru-papered and carpeted corridor. "The penthouse?" She cocked a blond brow.

"Not exactly," he humored her. "My apartment may be on the top floor, but it's only one of four." He put the key in the lock and turned it.

"I'm surprised you've been able to avoid condominium conversion. It seems to be the thing lately."

"I don't believe in it." He looked easily down at her. "To have to make that kind of financial investment and buy into responsibilities that many people don't want seems unfair. Many of these tenants are retired. They've had their day in the country. They've owned their own homes and now they want a simpler life."

"You have an understanding owner." Too late, she understood the twinkle in his eye.

"I *am* the owner. It helps." Grinning, he pushed the door open for her to enter.

Alanna was not quite prepared for the world of understated elegance in which she found herself. But then, why not? Wasn't the man himself a prime example of subtle class? Her eye skimmed the open foyer before being quickly drawn toward the large living room. The overall impression was one of cool serenity; the room had been decorated in a quiet blend of brown, navy and cream. There was a central sunken pit bounded by the plush cushions of a sectional sofa. There were side tables and étagères, each bearing exquisite groupings of small sculptures of stone or crystal. There was a long wall unit containing a bar, a stereo and scattered rows of books, and one entire wall was taken up by windows that looked out on the harbor.

"Well . . . what do you think?" His concern for her approval was endearing and impossible to resist.

"It's magnificent, Alex!" She beamed, turning to face him, first with enthusiasm, then mischief. "Now tell me that a lovely raven-haired beauty with whom you happened to be living at the time decorated it for you."

"No." He approached her. "*I* decorated it. I have specific tastes—in furnishings *and* in women."

"My compliments, then, on the furnishings," she quipped. "As for the women, since I haven't kept track of your entourage over the years I must withhold judgment."

"None of them come anywhere near you, Alanna," he vowed, his eyes dark and enticing.

Quickly, she mocked their sensuality. "Your brain must be addled by too *much* sleep—"

"—and I've never had a live-in lady," he interrupted, far more serious than she and determined to make his point.

She tipped her head in skepticism. "Never?"

"Never." He walked to stand before the wall unit and thrust his hands into his trouser pockets. His streamlined stance exaggerated his height. "I've always lived alone and preferred it that way. Until now." His eyes bore steadily into hers.

Ignoring his final words, she probed his feelings. "It must be difficult . . . living alone, taking care of all those things that a woman would normally do."

"Such as?" He was mildly amused.

Alanna shrugged. "You know, the cooking, cleaning, laundry . . ."

To her chagrin Alex's gaze narrowed and he stalked

toward her, very definitely on the attack. *"That* was a sexist statement if I've ever heard one. It's amazing. *You're* the only old-fashioned thing in this room!"

Of the many ways she had viewed herself over the years, old-fashioned had never been one. "What do you mean?"

"I mean that you obviously consider those chores as 'woman's work.' Did it ever occur to you that a man can do those things, too?"

"Do *you?*" she asked with a grin, instantly humored at the image of Alexander Knight folding laundry.

"I cook."

It came too freely. "And . . . the others?"

He waffled. "Well . . . I try not to . . . I have someone . . ."

"A woman?" she drove the point home.

Alex waved a hand as if to indicate the irrelevance of the matter. "As it happens, yes. She was all I could find at the time. But—"

"So who's old-fashioned?"

"You are!" He refused to back down. "If you decided to marry me it wouldn't mean that you'd be suddenly chained to the house. I'd still hire people to do those chores and that would free us both up for work . . . *and* play. You assume that every traditional responsibility would be yours. I'm saying that it just wouldn't be so."

"I know, Alex. I know." There was a momentary hint of resignation in her tone. Turning quietly, she wandered aimlessly about the room. "Even living by myself, I've had to make compromises to get things done in between work hours. I have help, too. But I somehow thought that men liked their women to do that kind of thing."

"There's where you're silly, love," he gently chided her. "When a man loves a woman he respects her, as well. I would no more force you to be a live-in maid than I would ask you to give up your career. Don't you see," he moved to stand before her, lifting his hands to curve around her neck, his thumbs steadying her chin, "I love you for what you *are*. I could never try to destroy or change that. The first time I saw you—in that elevator—I sensed the spirit in you that appeals so strongly to me. It's your strength, your independence, your intelligence and self-sufficiency—among other things—that I love."

Alanna's brown gaze climbed to meet his. "Perhaps it's the challenge you love, rather than *me*. I do know how you love a dare," she reminded him lightly.

"So do you."

"Uh-huh. But I don't confuse that with true love. The newness, the challenge, are bound to wear off. What happens then? Where does that leave you?"

If Alanna thought to stump Alex she was taken aback by his total preparedness. "It leaves *us* to seek out challenges together, to find new and exciting things together. We share the love of adventure; that's one of the things that binds us together. For the first time in my life I've found a woman who thrives on challenge as much as I do." His arms fell slowly to his sides; his words held their own weight.

Alanna had no proper retort. It stunned her to admit the merit of his argument. She, too, had never enjoyed a man as much as she did Alex—and for many of the same reasons. There was a good explanation for why she never dated a man more than once or twice; boredom encompassed much of it. Instinctively she knew that Alex Knight would never, *never* bore her.

It was hard enough to admit this to herself; she simply couldn't admit it to Alex. In search of diversion, her eye caught on the bookshelf. "Are you a thriller fan?" she asked, excited.

Alex spent a fast moment looking suspiciously from Alanna's brightened face to the books, then back. "Aren't we both? Suspense. Intrigue. Action. Romance. Mystery. Isn't that what life is all about?"

She avoided his question to study the collection before her. "I think you've got all my favorites." A tapered finger traced the spine of one of the volumes. "One thing's for sure." She smiled sheepishly. "Books like this never put me to sleep! Which brings up the immediate problem." Her gaze met his once more. "What are we going to do about the IAT study?"

"*That's* not really the immediate problem, love. The immediate problem is *us*. What are we going to do about *us*?"

A flicker of pain crossed her face. "That's very simple," she lied. "Nothing."

"Nothing?" he repeated her statement, his furrowed brow hinting at disagreement "What do you mean by that?"

"Exactly what I said. We're adults. I see no reason to get all bothered about things. Is there a rush?"

"What about last night?" he asked, his tone cool.

"What about it?"

"Didn't it mean anything to you?"

Disquieted and unable to lie on this point, she fled to the window. "Of course it did."

He was close on her heels. "What did it mean?" His reflection in the window, framed by the black of night, towered over hers.

Alanna gathered her thoughts, sorting out those she could share from those that, for the present, had to remain her own. "It meant that we are phenomenally attracted to one another. It meant that we shared something very special."

"I'll say it was special!" Alex exploded, grasping her shoulders and forcefully turning her to face him. "I've said I love you time and again. If you were honest you would return the vow. You do love me, Alanna. Last night proved it!"

To her chagrin he had hit on the core of her confusion. When she lashed out it was as much in argument with herself as with him. "That's being naive, Alex! Just because I let you make love to me doesn't mean I love you!"

"That's just it," his voice lowered to a calmer pitch, "you didn't just *let* me make love to you; you made beautiful love right back to me! No," he caught her tighter when she tried to pull away, "don't run this time. Face it. You felt something last night with me. You feel it right now. I can tell. That cool, suave woman I met in the cafeteria just the other night is not quite so cool and suave anymore. She's discovered that the core of passion she's squelched for years is not quite dead."

"Passion," she broke in, trying desperately to exhibit the coolness he accused her of having lost, "is very different from love. Passion is physical—"

"Not at the level we shared last night!" His face was taut. "Say it, Alanna. There was more to last night than just the physical. Say it. You do love me."

"I think I ought to leave."

"Why? Are you that frightened of yourself?"

"No!" She spoke honestly. "I'm frightened that you'll make me say things I simply don't feel."

"Or *think* you feel?"

She sighed in resignation. "Or *think* I feel."

When he released her she wandered to the sofa and let its deep cushions envelop her. Resting her elbow on the sofa's arm, she propped her forehead against her palm. It was nearly ten-thirty; her fatigue was emotional, rather than physical.

"I wish I could offer you coffee or a nightcap. . . ." Alex's voice was quiet, more controlled.

"I'm fine without."

"Can I get you *any*thing?"

She shook her head quickly, then continued to shake it more slowly. "I don't know what I'm doing here." The words poured forth unbidden. "I had my life perfectly organized. I was so proud of myself because I'd finally gone to the clinic. Insomnia . . . hah! Little did I suspect that I'd meet a crazy man who had an obsession with marriage!"

His large, tanned hands entered her vision as he propped them on the back of the sofa on either side of her. "He's intelligent . . ."

She shrugged faintly. "Perhaps . . ."

"And successful . . ." His voice was lower.

"Perhaps . . ."

"And good-looking . . ."

She grinned, much against her better judgment. ". . . and immodest . . ."

"Perhaps," he drawled in mockery, then dipped his head until his breath fanned her ear. "He also loves you very much."

The words tore at the defenses he'd already battered almost to shreds. She wasn't quite sure whether her moan was one of anger, frustration or pleasure. But when he rounded the sofa and sat down beside her she slid her arms about his waist and crumbled against him. "Why do you say things like that, Alex?"

"Because I mean them."

"But don't you know that I'm not *ready* for that yet?"

"Is that what's bothering you? The rush?"

She hesitated. "In part, yes."

"And the other part?"

"The other part has to do with my life, with everything I've worked for and everything I've built."

Alex's hand stroked her hair. "A relationship with me doesn't mean that you have to give that up."

"When the 'relationship' is marriage," she argued, "things change."

In the silence that followed the only thing she heard was the rapid thump of his heartbeat. It had a pacifying effect that she couldn't deny. Nor could she deny the vehemence in his tone when he did finally speak.

"You know, for a bright woman you're really being dumb! Where have you been, Alanna? It's not simply a matter of choosing between career and marriage. Women today can have both! I would never ask you to give ûp what you've worked so hard for and what means so much to you."

His words were reminiscent of those Jake Wallace had used in his office several days ago. From the lips of a man it sounded so simple. In the mind of a woman it was anything but.

"What about a family, Alex?" she asked, looking up at him. "Surely you want to have one?"

"Of course. Don't you?"

"I haven't wanted a husband, let alone children." *Until now.* Shock waves raced through her at the realization that, for the first time, she was actually contemplating the possibility with some seriousness "But even if I did, how would I handle it?"

"We could work it out."

"How? I put in ten-hour days as it is. How would a husband and family fit into that?"

Alex's arms released their pressure. "Where there's a will, Alanna, there's a way. Come the day you want a family, you'll find a happy compromise. Anything is possible—if you want it badly enough."

"Touché," she whispered, leaving his arms and leaning back against the sofa, closing her eyes to erase Alex's devastating presence.

"You're tired."

"I'm weary, if there's a difference. I've been thinking, thinking, thinking all day and I still can't see the light."

Gazing through the golden shade of her lashes she saw Alex lean forward and rest his elbows on his knees, one fist fitted snugly within the other palm. "Would you like me to take you home?" he asked, his jaw clenched.

Alanna looked at him, instantly knowing her answer. There was no need for in-depth soul-searching; every fiber of her being wanted to stay with him tonight. Her voice was soft and vulnerable. "No."

If Alex inhaled sharply, he camouflaged the gasp as quickly. "Why not, Alanna?"

She studied her fingers, surprised at their state of relaxation. "I'm not sure." She frowned in puzzlement before adding a soft, "I'd just rather stay here."

"Why?" When she offered nothing more than a mute sidelong glance he persisted. "You're pretty sure about the decision. Why not the reason behind it?"

"Perhaps I'm not as verbal about things as you are."

"Do you know that I've never talked as much to any person as I have to you? Do you know that I've always held things bottled up inside? One of the causes of insomnia is tension. One of the causes of tension is the internalization of thoughts and worries and problems. I've always done that. Yet I open up to you. *You* may know more about me, the *real* me, than any other person alive. Why is that?"

Alanna reflected on his words. "Perhaps I've asked you things that others haven't dared to ask." She stifled a smile.

"You're damned right!" He paused, contemplating the carpet for a moment before shaking his head and laughing. "The other night in the hospital cafeteria—do you remember what you said?" His gray eyes courted hers. "You said that you imagined me as the type who gave orders without having them questioned. I asked you if you'd question them and you assured me that you would. Do you remember?"

How could she forget any part of that conversation? She looked over at his shirt collar. "I seem to recall it, yes. . . ." Her eye wandered to the firm column of his neck until he leaned sharply forward and captured her gaze with his own insistent one.

"Well, I'm the one doing the questioning now. Why *don't* you want me to take you home?"

"I told you that I wanted to stay here. Isn't that enough?"

"No!"

"I'd rather not be alone."

"Why not? From what you've told me you've been alone for a long time and have done just fine."

Her pale brows met. "I have."

"Then what's changed now?" he persisted doggedly.

Alanna's voice rose in growing frustration. "I don't know!" She clearly sensed he sought some form of emotional commitment, but that was still beyond her reach.

It seemed that Alex's patience was waning. He was suddenly on the floor before her, clasping her hands. "Try to tell me, love. It's important. I *need* to know."

"How can I tell you something that I don't know myself?" she asked soulfully. "I do know that I enjoy your company, that for the first time in my life the thought of a quiet apartment sounds lonely and that I'd much rather be here with you. But beyond that, *what can I say?*"

As though temporarily sated by the mild sign of encouragement he sat back. If she had expected a smile of victory from him, however, she had underestimated his character. "You'll stay the night with me?" he asked warily.

Her answer was a whisper. "Yes."

"In my bed?"

"Yes."

He straightened and stood, looking down at her from what seemed an unreachable height. "You know what to expect if you stay." The dark charcoal of his eyes demanded an answer.

"I think so." Wasn't it what she wanted, too?

"And that doesn't bother you?"

"Should it?" she asked with a newer trepidation. "I've already admitted that we have something good together." Even now, staring up at the raw vision of masculinity before her, she felt a telltale tingle. "Is it wrong for me to give in to that pleasure?"

"You've avoided it all these years."

"Not wholly on principle. It's never seemed worth following through."

"Until now."

"That's right."

"And you feel comfortable about it . . . now?"

Alanna nodded, then repeated her query. "Am I wrong?"

"Not," he emphasized each word, "if you recognize the underlying emotion." His gaze was speculative. But regardless of its force she was unable to give a name to her feelings. She knew it. He knew it. "You won't marry me, yet you would *live* with me?"

She grew more cautious. "I thought the invitation was for one night. As far as *living* with you . . ."

"Would you?"

"I don't know." In truth, she didn't. There was some strong drive within that urged her to stay the night; a further commitment was something she would need time to consider.

Alex strode to the far side of the room. Alanna would have followed him had she known what to say. She had no explanation to give herself; how could she satisfy him? He turned to face her boldly, embodying every bit of the force she was sure had earned him many a corporate triumph.

"What if I said it was marriage or nothing?"

His words hung in the air like a storm before falling with devastation around her. Alanna was stunned. Had he trapped her? Was that what the intimacy of last night had been all about? Had he built up her awareness of him to a point of screaming need, a point where she would be unable to refuse his proposal of marriage? Was this a kind of emotional blackmail?

Trying a smile, she spoke softly. "I thought that was supposed to be *my* line."

He was fast with a comeback. "It *should* have been. But as you pointed out to me very clearly the first time we met, tradition is meaningless in this day and age. Well, I'm going to tell you something. Tradition may be out; I would never expect, or ask, you to be a *traditional* wife. But *commitment* is still in, in my book at least! That's what frightens you most, Alanna. Commitment. In your very defensive view one night at a time is fine. Anything more implies a commitment. And that's what you're trying to avoid, isn't it?"

"No. Not the way you put it."

"Then correct me."

Alanna stood to walk aimlessly around the room. Where could she begin? Anything she might say to him would be a spur-of-the-moment voicing of her own thoughts. There was so much she had yet to work out. Coming to a halt at the back of an armchair, she leaned on it for support, then moved around it to sit down.

"I never really knew my father." She sought the words that might explain. "He was a salesman, always on the road. It was just my mother and me for as long as I can remember." Alex's gaze leveled, then softened as he listened. "My mother was an intelligent woman. She read voraciously—anything she could get her hands on." A smile curved her lips at the memory. "I used to stop at the library twice a week on my way home from school to pick up books and magazines for her. She understood every nuance of politics and the economy— she was brilliant." She paused, anguish now clouding her features.

"When I was eighteen she took sick. I always wondered whether it was the fact that I had finally gone off to college. She had wanted that so badly for me—to get into a good school and leave Pittsburgh behind. Her single objective was to convince me to make something of my life, to be someone, to use my innate resources to the fullest, to move ahead in the world." Alanna cringed. "She thought of her own life as wasted."

Alex sought to disagree. "But how could it be—"

"It was!" she interrupted, displacing her anger from the time long past to him. "It was! She had so much going for her. Her only mistake was in loving my father."

"Alanna, that's an awful thing to say. How can you—"

Again she cut him off forcefully. "I *know* what I'm saying, Alex! I've had years to think about it—"

"—in the middle of the night?"

Understanding his implication, she smiled ruefully. "Yes, often in the middle of the night. There's so much anger and frustration, with no possible outlet." Her gaze fell to her hands, slender and clenched in her lap. She spoke more softly now, more thoughtfully. "I'm not talking ill of my father, merely claiming that he and my mother were grossly mismatched. He insisted that her place was in the home, raising me, waiting for his periodic appearances. She would never have gone against his wishes. So she did sit and wait . . . and wait . . . and wait. It was a waste of her intelligence."

"Was she unhappy?"

Alex stood close by her side now. When she raised her eyes they were clear and honest. "No. At least, I don't think she was *conscious* of being unhappy. She accepted her life because she loved my father. But the dreams she had for me—those had to express some inner feelings of hers. She never did complain, though. Never."

With a deep breath she looked away to continue the tale. "She was sick for three years. *He* stopped by when he happened to be in town, but it was mainly the two of us, as it had always been. I had transferred back to college in Pittsburgh so that I could be with her. She wasn't pleased about it, but she did need me there. But she never once let up on the theme that I should leave as soon as she died. It was as though," her voice wavered, "she purposely let go of life to free me." Dry-eyed, she looked toward the window. Alex's tall frame intercepted her gaze.

"Did you have any kind of relationship with your father after she died?"

Her blond head snapped back, eyes flashing in remembered vehemence. "No! I did what my mother wanted. I left Pittsburgh as soon after the funeral as I could."

"Do you think he suffered?"

"My father? At *my* leaving?"

"At your mother's death," he softly clarified his question.

"Oh, yes," she grimaced. "There was no one to meet him when he returned, to unpack his bags and wash everything, to make his meals and wait on him hand and foot, then pack his bags once more and send him off. I'm *sure* he missed her."

"You're very bitter."

It was precisely Alex's gentleness that emphasized the harshness of Alanna's indictment. Embarrassed, she averted her eyes. "I'm sorry. I didn't mean to sound that way. It's just . . . just . . ."

"What?"

She took a deep breath, voicing something she had never admitted, even to herself. "It's just that *I* needed someone then, too. My mother and I had been very close. Suddenly she was gone. For the first time I actually needed my father. But I was so frightened that I'd find myself in the role of caretaker, as my mother had been, that I never gave it a chance. Perhaps he would have risen to the occasion and been a comfort. I'll never know." Head low, she silently mourned that lost opportunity.

Alex's voice was smooth and low and as close by as she might have wished her father to have been so long ago. "You could give him the benefit of the doubt."

She smiled sadly. "I suppose I could."

The long silence that followed allowed her to gather her composure and she felt stronger when Alex took her chin and tilted it up for his study. "I'm glad you've shared this with me, Alanna. It helps me to understand why certain things mean so much to you, that powerful professional drive of yours, for one. But I still think you're wrong." He spoke gently, soothing her even as he expressed a differing opinion from hers. "I respect what your mother told you—and her need for telling you—but it's possible that, if she could see you now, today, having achieved what you have, she would tell you that there's more to life than a career. She told you to realize your potential and you have, in the professional sense. But what about your potential for loving? What about your potential for caring, which you showed when you sat by her bedside night after night after spending long days at school? What about the maternal instinct that she must have passed down to you?"

Helpless to twist her head away, Alanna could only hold his gaze. He painted a picture of a different kind of existence and she could no more summarily dismiss it than she could turn her back and walk away from him.

Did he have a point? *Was* she missing something? Her eyes, brown and luminous, reflected the inner turmoil which he sought to understand.

"I also see that you're right," he conceded quietly. When her brows furrowed in confusion he explained. "You do need time. This has happened much too quickly." But he would yield only so much ground before he reasserted his own sentiment. "I'm convinced that you do love me. In time you'll come to see that, too."

"How can you be so sure?" she cried in exasperation.

"Sure that you love me? There are several ways. Right now I can tell from your eyes."

"My eyes?"

He nodded, sending a dashing swathe of brown hair lower onto his forehead. "They're dry. You just spoke of your mother and of a very painful time in your life. It had to be difficult to recall it, but you didn't cry."

"I never cry—" She fell quickly into his trap.

"You did last night. If I'm correct that was the first time in years. *Am* I correct?"

He had begun to encroach more deeply on things that had puzzled her all day. Yet she could not deny the truth. "Yes."

To her astonishment a slow smile spread across his face, lighting it magnificently. "I'm glad, Alanna. Don't you see? The fact that you were able to cry out all that hurt and anger and loneliness to *me,* of all people, says something. The fact that you made love to me," he arched one brow, "says something, too."

She couldn't argue.

He paused and slid his arms around her, drawing her up to stand against him. "When you first told me about Harding you said you had loved him."

"I thought I did . . . at the time." Her voice was muffled against the warmth of his shirt and the broad expanse of chest beneath. The sweet nearness of him blinded her to this latest trap.

"Were you disturbed when you broke up?" He spoke softly against her hair, seemingly content to hold her close.

"At first I was. But I got over it very quickly. I think that's when I realized that what I'd felt was not quite love. . . ."

"You didn't rush off to get involved with anyone else. . . ."

"No. I told you, I've never felt strongly enough about anyone . . ." At last, she caught his train of thought and her words drifted off.

Alex smiled, tentatively at first, then more broadly. "You see? That's another sign of your love for me. You let *me* know you."

"You trapped me into that," she pouted, more disturbed than angry.

"But it stands. You aren't a loose woman, Alanna. You wouldn't have stayed with me last night if you hadn't felt something special. And you certainly wouldn't agree to stay with me tonight just for the fun of it!"

"Fun—hah!" She sought refuge in mockery. "All you want to do is lecture me."

"That's not all I want to do and you well know it." The hands that pressed her insinuatingly against him elaborated meaningfully. "I love you, Alanna. I'm not afraid to say it. Nor am I afraid to show it." With that he swept her into his arms and sauntered toward the hallway leading off the living room.

"Alex!" she cried, squirming only until his arms tightened. "Aren't you being a little overdramatic? I mean, I *can* walk."

"Just setting precedent, love. I'm going to enjoy carrying you to bed over the years."

"Alex . . . you agreed not to push. . . ."

Her feet touched the thick pile carpet of his bedroom. "So I did," he drawled quite unrepentantly. "Now don't move!" He moved to adjust the lights until a single recessed fixture cast its gentle illumination around the room. Alanna had time only to absorb the masculine aura of the bold chocolates and whites of walls, rugs and furnishings before he deftly flipped back the dark-patterned bedspread and returned to her. His hands framed her face as he kissed her long and hard, stealing her breath with the force of his emotion. "Now," he crooned deeply, drawing his head back far enough to let him encompass all of her in his gaze, "I intend to show you exactly how much I love you."

"How much you *think* you love me," she returned in a whisper, referring to their earlier argument. At her smile his eyes narrowed, small crinkles of mischief radiating out from their corners.

"That's not even worth an argument, Alanna. But you keep telling yourself that. Maybe it will temper your response. . . ."

There was something challenging in his tone and in

the dark charcoal-gray beams that seared into her intensely. "Are you trying to tell me something that I don't already know, Alex?"

"What I'm doing," he rejoined without pause, "is daring you to keep that upper lip steady. I'll just bet you can't lie before me and be passive. Though if you don't love me it shouldn't be that hard to resist a response."

"Come on," she chided, "you know that the body has a will of its own, Alex."

"But your will is strong, love. If you work hard enough to show me that your feelings for me fall short you should be able to stay still, regardless of what I do."

"You make it sound dangerous," she quipped nervously.

"Are you up to the bet? While I show you how much I do love you, you can show me how much you *don't* love *me*."

"This is foolish."

"Ready to give in already?"

"No way!" She stiffened her spine, driven by frustration to resist him. "You aren't all *that* irresistible, you know." With a deep breath she drew herself up even straighter. Chin tilted at a bold angle, hands fallen loosely by her sides, eyes lit in defiance, she waited, offering herself as a willing opponent. If for no other reason than to take him down a peg or two, she was determined to withstand the sensory onslaught that she knew would follow. Unfortunately she had underestimated the force of his determination.

Alex was the consummate master, speaking volumes

with his eyes as he moved to within inches of her, leaving her shaking before he'd even touched her. His hands were gentle as they tipped her face up, his lips sweet in possession. She relaxed instinctively against him, then caught herself up short. His mouth opened wider, consuming her lips with thorough care, seeming to drain them of every bit of the rigidity she tried to instill. When her lips parted limply his tongue plunged within to probe the recesses of her inner warmth. Alanna steeled herself against the tantalizing foray, but darting tongues of desire licked at her nerve ends in a passion now far beyond her control.

Still she resisted. She reminded herself of his challenge and of what was at stake. But Alex's kiss taunted her for her futile attempt at concentration, tugging at her lips one final time as he drew back to look down at her. The pale light gentled his features, imbuing him with an aura of innocence.

"Not bad, owl-eyes." He grinned his compliment to her marginal success. He seemed undaunted and undisturbed, not in the least discouraged. Oh, yes, she mused, Alex Knight thrived in the ring! Reaching up, he removed her glasses and placed them carefully onto the shelf that comprised the headboard of the bed. Alanna watched his lazy motion, sensing in his languor its intended sensuality. His every move was smooth and fluid, athletic prowess in his every step. Helplessly she surveyed his lean frame, appreciating anew his head-to-toe virility, then telling herself of her immunity to it—between traitorous palpitations of her heart.

He took great pains with her hair, removing each pin, gathering them in a cluster in his palm and placing the lot on his dresser before finally combing the spill of blond silk with his fingers. As though enchanted he spread the strands about her shoulders.

"You seem to be operating in slow motion tonight. Are you enjoying yourself?" she asked evenly, dismayed when the indifference she had tried to inject into her voice emerged as impatience.

Alex grinned wickedly. "Every . . . last . . . minute."

Plunging his fingers into the thickness of her hair, he brought her lips to his once more. And this time he kissed her with a passion that left her dizzy. Dizzy and feeling heady. For with the knowledge that she could draw this man out to his fullest came pure delight. In this state of satisfaction Alanna responded reflexively.

"Uh-uh," he chided against her lips. "Giving up already?"

"No. No!" She caught herself up once again. "Just relaxing for a minute. It won't happen again."

"Don't let it," he drawled in warning, "or you'll never make it. You've got to be strong!"

She tried. Oh, how she tried! She tried to ignore the lips that tickled her neck and throat. She tried to ignore the fingers that reached for the zipper of her dress. She tried to ignore the eroticism of his long, drawn-out siege as he slid it slowly down, his fingers feathering along the line of her spine. It was very, very difficult.

He had to feel the wild beat of her heart when his hands slid beneath the fabric of the dress and around her shoulders, coaxing the fabric down, following to hold the fullness of her breasts. This time she gasped aloud.

"So soon, love?" he goaded her mischievously. "This is nothing!"

Nothing? Nothing the faint roughness of his finger-tips as they crept under the lace of her bra to tease her nipple to arousal? Nothing the thumbs that then dipped beneath the straps to lower them and allow her taut, round breasts to fall free? Nothing the mouth that trailed down her neck and nibbled at her shoulder blade before taking those hardened tips, first one, then the other, within?

Alanna barely stifled another cry. When Alex drawled a smug accusation she was quick to explain the hands that clutched his shoulders. "I'm not respond-ing," her singsong tone wavered. "I'm only trying to hold myself up."

"No need." Nudging her backward, he followed her easily onto the bed, covering her body with his. As he kissed her again he purposely let her feel the weight of his body. Alanna balled her fists in frustration. She ached to run her palms along the length of him, to feel the swell of his muscles and the texture of his skin against her fingertips. She wanted to kiss his flesh and taste the tang that was his alone. All she could do, however, was to lie in muted agony, breathing in his manly scent, struggling not to give in to the piercing arrows of need. When his lips finally left hers she moaned.

"Throwing in the towel, love?"

"Oh, no," she gasped. "No."

His mouth silenced her as his hands went back to work, dispensing with her bra and her remaining clothes with a haste that hinted at a certain gratifying wear and tear on *his* composure. Dress, slip, panty hose—all fell to the floor in the flurry. Then, his chest heaving slightly, he stood back to savor her.

"Your hands are clenched, Alanna. Is something wrong?"

Alanna was ready to explode from within. "No, no. What could be wrong? What could be more natural—"

"—than to lie naked before your lover?" he finished for her, expressing her unwilling thought precisely. His eyes caressed her beauty, beaming a molten heat along her skin.

Alanna swallowed thickly. She hadn't pictured herself as a sacrifice to the gods, yet here she was, helpless. Infinitely vulnerable and frantically clutching at the last straws of control. Was there, as Alex claimed, more to the attraction than the purely physical?

In a move that was subliminally arousing, Alex deftly shrugged off his suit jacket and draped it casually over a nearby chair. Alanna's throat constricted as she watched lean, male fingers draw off an already loosened tie. Those same fingers moved over the buttons of his shirt, releasing each, pulling the tails from his pants, tossing the shirt aside. His chest was a bold expanse of bronze lightly hazed with brown; his arms were sinewed and strong. She wanted to throw herself at him then; only his relentlessly watchful gaze restrained her.

Her mouth was dry. Absently she moistened her lips with the tip of her tongue. She watched helplessly as his hands moved to his belt, unbuckling it, unfastening his trousers. Within moments he stood before her, as nude as she. And then he approached. Propping himself on flattened palms, he leaned with maddening grace toward her.

"How can you be so cruel?" she rasped hoarsely, nearing the end of her tether.

"Cruel?" He feigned hurt. "It's not every day that I strip for a woman."

"Thank heaven!" she whispered, then waited for him to lower himself further. "Well . . . ?"

His grin was a knowing one. "Well what?"

Pride slipped inexorably through her whitened fingers until she was left with only the agony of wanting him. "Aren't you going to come to me?"

"In time." His answering whisper was low.

"Alex . . ." It was half warning, half pleading, inspired by her awareness of the bronzed perfection looming over her. He was inches away . . . yet too far. At that moment she knew him to be the key—the key to release the lock that barred her from fulfillment. It no longer mattered that, prior to meeting him, she hadn't even known the lock was in place. What mattered was that she needed him now.

With that realization went the last shreds of her tattered control. Reaching for him, she bridged the distance in an instant and stretched against him, coiling her arms tightly around his neck. Her weight, light as it was, brought his body down on top of hers, but not his head. That was tipped back so that he could see her clearly.

"You admit defeat?" He baited her one last time.

And Alanna reveled in that defeat. "I lose, I lose!" she declared with a conviction that was replaced by urgency when she touched him. Her hands hungered and devoured, making up for what seemed a lost eternity. To her further joy her loss of control triggered his. With a deep and soulful groan he made her his. The heat of the union fused them together, binding them as they moved to the age-old rhythm of passion. Forgotten now was the game they had played, its outcome secure from the start.

Alanna responded to Alex with the fullness of her womanhood. She drew on her intuitive resources to drive him to higher and higher peaks of ecstasy. And he had no intention of leaving her behind. She went with him avidly, her damp body clutched tightly to his. When at last the moment of ultimate delight exploded within and between them it cast its love-glow to enhance the climactic beauty they shared.

Their paired breathlessness slowly receded before Alex attempted to speak. His husky whisper was offered against her brow as he rolled onto his side and drew her against him. "You didn't lose after all, did you, love?"

There was no need for an answer. Her satisfied smile said it all.

Chapter Seven

No, she certainly hadn't lost. But what had she won? She had won long moments of shimmering ecstasy, then utter fulfillment. She had won the joy of having satisfied Alex as well, of feeling his body, warm and content, against hers. And she had won another night of deep and uninterrupted sleep. Wrapped in Alex's arms she felt replete and protected. A sweet serenity filled her through those hours, a sense of peace which held her even when he woke her with a kiss the next morning.

"Rise and shine, love. Time to get up." His voice tickled her ear with its early morning huskiness. Lazily, she burrowed closer.

"What time is it?"

"Six-fifteen."

"Six-fifteen?" Her brown eyes widened. "Why so early?"

Alex seemed amused. "We're going swimming. Remember?"

"Oh, no! That's right! Alex, what are we going to do

157

about the IAT study? We didn't settle *anything* last night!"

His drawl was suggestive. "I wouldn't say that. I seem to recall that you lost a certain bet. . . ."

"You're darned right I lost! It just shows you how taken I am with your body!" She grinned, knowing that she was skirting the issue but shooting for the diversion nonetheless. Alex saw right through her.

"Don't give me that, Alanna. You love me. Say it."

"What's in a word?" She shrugged with feigned nonchalance.

"A lot. Now say it. You love me."

Alanna nestled lower against him, helplessly admiring the soft skin just under his arm. When she touched it with a slim fingertip he squirmed. "You're ticklish!" she exclaimed, pleased to have found another diversion. But again Alex was determined to have his way.

He shifted lithely to capture her hands in one of his and immobilize her against his body with the other. "I'm very ticklish and even more in love." His eyes, gray and keen, repeated the demand he'd already made twice this morning. She knew what he wanted to hear, but couldn't quite say it. It would mean the commitment she had always feared.

"What *is* love?"

His answer was ready. "Love is when you want to do for and give to and put another's welfare ahead of your own. Love is when your life's meaning comes to revolve around that other person."

"And yours has?" She eyed him skeptically.

His grasp loosened, but without granting total release. "I know that you refuse to believe this, but it has.

On the surface I have everything most people want—a successful business, an apartment in the city, a home in the country, enough money to satisfy me. In a nutshell, I have every material thing I could want." She sensed what was coming. "But it's not enough. There's that awful emptiness that I've lived with for years. Frankly, I'm tired of it."

"So I'm a stopgap measure?"

"You know you're not, Alanna." He raised himself solemnly on one elbow. "And this is no time for joking. I've already told you some of the things about you that I love. Well, here's another. You've awakened in me a kind of protectiveness, a need to devote myself totally to one woman. I've never felt this way before."

As his eyes blazed their intensity toward her Alanna felt at war with herself. One side of her wanted to still his confession, to capture the thoughts and emotions he had roused and put them into a more easily controllable dimension. But the other side wanted to hear every word and more; this side hungrily savored his evident devotion. The battle raged within as Alex mused on.

"I'm thirty-nine years old, Alanna. I suppose I've been ready for a wife and family for a long time, but it's never appealed to me until now. I want *you* as my wife. I want *you* as the mother of my children. But mostly I want you with me every day, to share the business, this apartment, that house in the country."

The gentleness of his hand as it outlined her features was in contrast to the fire in his eyes. "Do you know what I want to do?" She couldn't tear her gaze away; mutely she shook her head. "I want to bring you breakfast in bed on the weekends and sit here beside you reading the paper. I want to drop you at work in the morning and pick you up at night and spend every possible minute in between making you happy."

"You're crazy," she whispered, but her smile held undeniable affection.

Alex lay down flat once more and pulled her head to his shoulder to continue the dream. "I may be, but it *is* how I feel. I want to buy you things—little extravagances that you'd never buy for yourself—and take you places. I'd like to travel with you to all the exotic spots you've never taken the time to visit."

"I'm not exactly deprived," she argued feebly.

"I know that! No doubt you could easily afford to take those trips yourself. Why haven't you? For one thing, you won't leave that job of yours for long enough because you're afraid that some ambitious man will steal it from you. For another, though you may not be willing to admit it, it's no fun to travel alone."

Alanna couldn't lie. She'd thought often of travel and had vetoed it for just those reasons. "I admit it," she conceded softly.

"Then," he continued more gently, "why won't you admit that, together, we could have a lovely life."

"Because I'm just not sure of that yet."

"Even after last night?"

"Yes. Lovemaking is still a physical act. Love entails more. Don't you see, Alex?" She raised herself on an elbow to look down at him beseechingly. "I've lived my life alone for so long. I've been totally independent. I rely on no one. Love has never been high priority with me."

His voice was even. "Then you don't love me?"

"I don't know."

In the silence that followed, Alanna acknowledged, for the first time, that she could easily come to love Alex—if she didn't already do so. As she recognized the vulnerability in his face now her only impulse was to soothe it. Yes, in many respects, if Alex's definition was apt, she was in love. She did want to give to him, to share with him, to do for him. Yet there was still that other life. . . .

He sighed deeply, studying her confused expression for a moment longer. Then he smiled, that broad, white-toothed smile that set her heart to beating double-time. "Now we're getting somewhere. An 'I don't know' is far better than an outright 'No'!" He threw back the covers and got out of bed, turning to face her with no thought at all to his nudity. "I'll get to you yet, Alanna. You may think you have it all now, but you'll be thinking differently soon. *I'll* show you."

Alanna half believed him. To her perplexity, she half *wanted* to believe him. He was, in so many ways, not the least of which was the image of bold masculinity he presented to her now, a divine creature. Her gaze luxuriated in his body for a final moment as she lay in bed. Then, without warning, his hands whipped off her covering and curved under her, lifting her from the bed and setting her upright just outside the bathroom. His release was slow; her body slithered sensuously down his in poignant remembrance of the passion they'd shared the previous night. He kissed her deeply, his lips inviting her waiting response.

"We'll never get *anywhere* at this rate," he finally growled against her moist lips. "You go in there; I'll use the other one. We'll meet in the living room in ten minutes. Can you do it?"

"Anything you can do I can—"

"All right, all right! Just *be* there!"

Such playfulness was a rarity in either of their early-morning experiences. Alanna pondered it with pleasure as she dressed quickly, then joined him for the drive to the pool. An hour later, as they sat down to breakfast, they talked of the IAT study. It was Alex who voiced their shared opinion.

"I think that we ought to let Ellen fill our places with two other people. We seem to have temporarily solved our problem." His eyes twinkled with a silver light. "That's two nights in a row . . . the first time in years for me."

"Same here." She couldn't disagree. "But why? Is it," she blushed, continuing against her better judgment, "simply a matter of physical exhaustion?"

Alex reached across the table to take her hand in his. Her skin seemed pale against his tan, her fingers that much more fragile. "You know better than that. Even the swimming isn't so much for the sake of exhaustion as for letting out pent-up frustration. And our love-making takes it one step further."

"To where?" She cornered him, relying on his apparent talent for expression to help her sort out her own jumbled thoughts.

"To the point of satisfying a need. On my part," he looked closely at her, "it's a need to love and have the person I love with me. Do you remember I told you about those feelings I used to wake up to?" When she nodded he went on. "They've been gone completely these last two nights. When I wake up in the morning I feel filled, not empty."

Alanna looked away. His self-analysis came too close to describing the feelings she had experienced herself. It bothered her that he felt so much freer about expressing them, yet she couldn't help herself. As though understanding her dilemma and willing to grant her more time to resolve it, Alex didn't push for a similar confession. Rather, his talk returned to the immediate matter of Ellen Henderson and her study.

"I'll call her this morning and explain things. You do agree that we should drop out, don't you?"

"Yes. For now, at least. She was right; there have been so many new factors introduced since we agreed to participate that it would skew the results anyway. And if we can continue to sleep through the night . . ."

"Which brings up that other issue." He paused to offer her a warm sweet roll from the basket that the waiter had just brought. She accepted and began to butter it as he mirrored her actions. Both knew what this other issue entailed; both were somewhat unsure, each in his own way. Again it was Alex who took the lead.

"You know that I want to marry you, Alanna." He waited for her nod before continuing. "If you agreed we could be married this weekend and then there would be no question about living apart. But you won't agree . . . not yet. Which leaves us with three possibilities."

She put down her roll, suddenly not as hungry as she had been.

"Eat!" Alex's order startled her.

"I'm not hungry."

"You need something to carry you through the day, Alanna. Don't be difficult."

"I've ordered an omelet. It should be here any minute."

His voice lowered. "I know that, but the rolls are good."

Alanna sighed in frustration. "Alex, what's the problem? Why don't you just get on with what you have to say?"

That was it; she saw it the instant she said it. He was, in his way, as apprehensive as she was about making plans, yet they had to do it. Perhaps she could help him.

Her voice was soft, but loud enough to allow him to catch every word. "You're right. We have three possibilities. We either live together—without benefit of marriage, see each other on occasion or go our separate ways."

"Right." The one word was spoken tensely, all his vulnerability evident.

Alanna thought aloud. "I'd like to rule out the last."

Alex was quick to challenge her. "Do you admit that you can't live without me?"

"That's not the point." She kept her voice down and lowered her eyes. He might have been right, but she couldn't even admit it to herself, much less to him. "But if we don't see each other we'll never be able to work *any*thing out. And if we don't see each other we'll probably both start waking up at night again and therefore ought to stay in the study. . . ."

"All right," he conceded quickly, reluctant to let

things get more complicated than they already were. "Strike going our separate ways." His deep breath could as easily have been a sleepy yawn as an expression of relief. "What next?"

Alanna was far from helpless. Systematically she attacked the next possibility. "As far as living together, I doubt that you would stand for that." Her gaze held faint accusation.

"You're very perceptive. And do you know why I wouldn't stand for it?" Without awaiting her guess he went on, lowering his voice only when her eyes flew to the tables surrounding theirs. "Because I think that that would be the easy way out for you and I won't let you take it. When it gets to the point that you want to spend every free minute of your life with me, that you want to sleep with me *every* night and wake up with me *every* morning, you can damn well confess your love and marry me!"

"Shhh! Keep it down, Alex!"

He leaned closer and spoke more softly, but the vehemence was still there. "I don't particularly care *who* hears me! I love you!"

"I know," she sighed. "You've told me so more than once."

And she believed him. Finally. He *did* love her and the sudden realization gnawed at her. She knew instinctively that Alex Knight would do nothing halfheartedly. If he loved her he would love her with everything he possessed. It was a beautiful thought, but one that was also terrifying. For while one part of her wanted very much to return his love, the other part fought it with every bit of the strength that she had had a lifetime to accrue.

"Where does that leave us?" he asked more gently, back in control. "We see each other *on occasion?*" Skepticism was written on his every feature. "Just what does that mean?"

She grinned, relieved that his acute vulnerability seemed to have passed. For it was to that vulnerability that she herself was acutely vulnerable. "It permits you—us—the pleasure of each other's company when the opportunity arises—"

"Such as tonight?" he rebounded. "For dinner?"

"I'd like that." She accepted his invitation softly.

"Then," he sat back more confidently, "I'm to 'woo' you?" A hint of mischief entered his gaze.

"You make it sound so Victorian."

His mouth slanted wryly. "It's not quite what I would have expected from a modern woman. I wouldn't have called your behavior last night, or the night before, for that matter, exactly Victorian."

Alanna chose to ignore his barb, growing suddenly more sober. "I need time, Alex. You said so yourself. I need breathing space. If, as you hope," she verged on sarcasm, "I'm to discover that I simply can't live without you, I'll have to spend time with you *and* time away, won't I?"

Alex hesitated, then agreed reluctantly. "I suppose you will. But remember, I can only be *so* patient. And I do get jealous. I don't want you dating other men."

Without thinking she bristled; then she thought. Slowly a coy grin spread from ear to ear. He liked a challenge, did he? "What's wrong, Alex? Are you worried that, in comparison to another man, there might be something lacking in your appeal?"

His protest went no further than a quickly indrawn breath. He was sharp; he saw what she was up to in the instant, but their breakfast, hot and fresh from the kitchen, was placed in front of them before he had a chance to answer.

As soon as the waiter had gone he spoke. "If I said no you would think I was arrogant. If I said yes you would think I was insecure. In truth, I'm neither. I'm more concerned with *my* thoughts, knowing that another man's hands might be touching you. But," his gaze enveloped her speculatively, "on second thought, I think I'll take my chances. See whoever you want; it can only help my cause."

Her "Speaking of arrogance . . ." was muffled behind a mouthful of cheese omelet. Beyond that she let the matter ride. She didn't want to see anyone else, anyway. Her objection had been to his command; it was a matter of principle. Once the command had been revoked she had no desire to rebel against it.

Following breakfast Alex dropped her back at the hospital lot to pick up her car with a promise to stop by her apartment at seven-thirty that evening. She went contentedly on to work, breezing through the day with more patience and endurance than she'd felt in months. Jake commented on her improved outlook when he dropped by her office to talk late in the afternoon.

"You're looking chipper today, Alanna. You must be sleeping better."

She smiled sweetly, trying to hold in her secret. "I am."

"How's Alex?" he asked with a nonchalance she knew to be a sham.

"Fine." Again she smiled.

"Still after you?" He settled his slightly rounding frame into a nearby chair.

"Uh-huh."

"Are you still resisting?"

"Now, Jake. That's getting a little more personal than usual, don't you think?"

"Just answer me; are you still fighting him?"

"On the matter of marriage," she chose her words with care, "yes. On the matter of getting acquainted," *what an appallingly inadequate word that was,* she mused, "no."

"Good. You know, he could help you when I move you up into the Executive Vice-President's slot."

"Are you still serious about that, Jake?"

"Very serious. The meeting is Monday. And if I propose you, you're in."

She shook her head, though not a wisp of her neatly coiled blond hair budged. "I don't know, Jake . . . I appreciate the thought, but it could cause more of a problem among the men here than it's worth."

Jake Wallace sat back in his chair and studied her closely. "Don't you want the promotion?"

She shrugged. "I'm doing the work, anyway. . . ."

"Then why shouldn't you get the credit?" he asked sharply.

"It just doesn't seem to matter—the title, I mean. If I have the power now to set into action—and keep in action—the projects I think are promising, what more can I ask?"

"You can ask," Jake went on insistently, "for recognition and respect from those men!"

"Hah! They'll give that to me when and if they feel like it! A promotion will only get their tails up!"

Jake's voice lowered. "That's where Knight comes in."

"What?"

"Alex Knight. Marry him. That will end all speculation about your . . . ah . . . extracurricular activities at my house."

Alanna rolled her eyes skyward, not quite sure she'd heard her mentor correctly. "Jake, you've been happily married now for some thirty-odd years. Would *you* have gotten married for a reason like that?"

He held his breath expectantly, then narrowed his gaze. "Not unless I loved the person I was proposing to marry."

Her sculpted features were momentarily pained; quickly she turned away from Jake. "That's just the issue. Alex loves me. I . . . I'm not so sure of my own feelings."

Despite the inconclusiveness of her answer, Jake was satisfied. "I can't tell you what you feel, Alanna. But I can tell you this: When I walked in here a few minutes ago you had that very special look about you. No," he halted her protest, "I wasn't imagining it." Then he feigned sternness. "And don't tell me that it was excitement about the biotechnics project. You've been pleased about projects before, but you haven't looked like this."

"You're reading too much—"

"Oh, no." He shook his head stubbornly. "I know you, Alanna. There's been a change."

"I'm sleeping well." Her smile returned; they were back to square one.

"So you told me." He cleared his throat. "Alanna," he stood, "you're nearly as pigheaded as Elaine when she sets her mind to something. In this case, it's 'the works' at the beauty shop on Saturday. She's hoping that you'll join her for lunch afterward. What time do you finish at the pool?"

After some quick mental calculations Alanna relaxed. "If I drop her there at nine, I can pick her up by one. There's a swim meet at ten; it shouldn't last more than two hours."

When Jake shook his head this time it was in admiration. "You're amazing, my girl. And have I told you lately how much I appreciate what you do for Elaine? I could drive her myself, but she seems to think that this is women's business. It's hard enough for her to cope with that wheelchair; she feels so dependent. Somehow you make her feel as though she's no imposition. Frankly, I don't know what we'd *both* do without you."

Alanna gave her hand to Jake as she walked with him to the door. "The feeling's mutual; you know that. It's so important for her to lead as normal a life as possible. Driving her on Saturday is the least I can do. And, yes, do tell her that I'd love to join her for lunch."

On Saturday Alanna drove Elaine to the beauty shop, then shared a late lunch with her at a nearby restaurant. Over Potage St. Germaine and salads of fresh endives and almonds they talked with the comfort of old friends—of what was happening at the office *and* after hours. Elaine was eager to hear about the swim team's victory over its opponent and Alanna was too pleased with the triumph to deprive her of the details. When the subject of Alexander Knight came up, however, Alanna was caught off guard. Afterward she realized that Jake would have shared such an interesting tidbit with his wife and she felt no actual regret. Her words were measured, though, and Elaine was unable to pass on any more to Jake than he already knew.

It was late afternoon when she finally had her friend safely returned to the Wallace home. Then she stopped at the supermarket, the dry cleaner and the florist for a bunch of fresh daisies to replace those that had withered in the vase atop her table. The pale gold November sun spilled across her champagne carpet when she sat, at last, quiet and by herself in her own home. Only then did her thoughts return to Alex.

In a slow motion replay of the night before she found herself snowed afresh by the devastating charm and virile appeal of the man. When Alex had mentioned dinner she'd assumed they'd be going out. But he'd had something quite different in mind when he had picked her up and returned her to his place. As it happened, even *his* plans were superseded by a spontaneous demonstration of talents other than culinary.

Alanna was still not quite sure what had taken them immediately to bed in each other's arms, their dinner temporarily forgotten. She blushed at the memory of their abandon. Perhaps, from her viewpoint, it had been the way he had looked in casual dress—jeans and a turtleneck sweater, both of which were alarming to her senses in the snug way they fit.

When they finally returned to the kitchen, hand in hand, Alanna wore nothing but Alex's turtleneck; he wore the jeans alone.

Even now the scent of him filled her nostrils—that musky male tang that spiced his bed, his towels, that warm, oversized turtleneck sweater that fell to her thighs. Tingling, she blushed again, then fought the tide of rising sensation. It simply wasn't fair for this man—*any* man—to wield such power! That she should tremble now at the memory of their passion was mind-boggling!

It had, indeed, been a night to remember. There was not only a jointly produced feast of sukiyaki, rice and cucumber salad to devour, there was Beethoven's *Eroica* to soothe them and a bright birch fire to hypnotize. When they returned to bed it was to a round of lovemaking that, by some miracle, surpassed the others in pure rapture. It was as though Alex read every soft nuance of her body, delighting in each secret dare, each hidden challenge. For Alanna the game was reciprocal. She discovered that his hard man's body had similar soft spots; it was her joy to seek them out.

Once again they slept through the night and once again it was Alex's kiss that awakened her in the morning. The routine, she had mused, could easily become habit-forming.

The jangle of the telephone brought her from her reverie and back to the early evening quiet of her apartment.

"Hello?"

"Hey, owl-eyes," the deep voice flowed silkily over the wire, "how are you?"

How familiar and good his voice sounded! "I'm fine." She smiled in response, though she knew he couldn't see. "How did everything go today?" Alex had flown south early that morning for a series of emergency meetings in Atlanta.

"Slow, love. That's why I'm calling."

She read fatigue, perhaps even a hint of discouragement, in his voice and was instantly concerned. "What's wrong? Did something happen?"

"No. Everything is going all right. Just slow. Very slow. Making agreements with this nine-member board is like taking a photograph of a thirty-member family and getting everyone to smile."

"They don't like your proposal?" His humor soaring above her, Alanna was stunned. Alex had explained the fundamentals of the project, one that would merge the brains of a think-tank center in Atlanta with the money of the Knight Corporation to study problems of social welfare. It was such a worthwhile cause. . . .

"They seem to like it," Alex explained gently, "but they differ among themselves as to whether one organization—mine—should be the sole affiliate. Several of the board members believe that they should receive funding on a problem-by-problem basis."

"But that would be such a waste of time and effort!"

"I know that," his low voice rejoined, "and you know that, but try telling it to them." He sighed. "But that's what I intend to do tonight, if possible. . . ." Alanna caught his drift immediately.

"Tonight?" He had tentatively suggested that morning that they would spend the evening together when he returned. "Then you'll be staying in Atlanta?"

His voice was guarded, as though he were unsure of her reaction and wary of showing his own feelings. "I've got to. It's got to be taken care of soon or there'll be twice as much work later." He paused, his tone finally softening. "I'm sorry. I was looking forward to being with you."

Alanna was caught in a whirlpool of emotion, anger and hurt and sorrow swirling round and round each other. In the end she could only sigh. "I am, too."

"I'm hoping to get back by tomorrow afternoon. Will I see you then?" Again he was cautious.

"I can't, Alex. I have tickets for the afternoon show at the Players' Theater."

"You're going alone?" She could almost see his angry glare.

"No. I'm going with two friends—"

"*Male* friends?" *Male* sounded positively evil.

"Alex! Did I ask you how many of the board members you're seeing are women?" She took a breath to steady her suddenly shaky pulse. "It happens that we've had these tickets for two months. And I'm going to the *matinée,* not the midnight show."

"Then I'll take you to dinner afterward," he offered, temporarily pacified.

"We're already going to dinner afterward," she explained patiently. "These are good friends, but I don't get to see them as often as I'd like."

"Are they business contacts?"

"Actually, no. I met them several years ago through

a literature course I took at the university. Diana is a high school teacher; Maxine has a doctor-husband and two young children at home."

There was no audible sigh of relief; the lightening of Alex's tone alerted Alanna of just how worried he had been. "That sounds nice. Where will you be eating?"

Alanna's suspicions were sparked by the pointedness of the question. "I . . . don't . . . know. . . ." She drew out the words, each pause relaying the idea that she had no intention of spilling *that* information as well.

"OK, love." He sounded cheerful enough, satisfied with winning one out of two. "I've got to run. Will you miss me tonight?"

"I may just lie awake all night and pine for you." Her answering drawl buried truth deep within its good humor.

Alex saw it quickly. "It should be interesting, you know."

"What?"

"Seeing what kind of a night's sleep we have. This will be the first time we've slept apart in—"

"I know, Alex. I know." His words stirred images she felt were best left alone at the moment. "Just remember not to drink liquor or coffee." Her tone playfully mocked Ellen Henderson's directives. "Don't go to bed until you're tired. Don't lie in bed for more than ten minutes without—"

"All right, Alanna! That's enough! You sound like a mother hen! Just remember that those instructions apply to *you*, too! I'll talk with you tomorrow night, then?"

"That sounds fine." She hesitated, reluctant to say

good-bye. "Good luck with your meetings." Humor always helped. "I know you'll charm the skirts off them!" She wasn't prepared for Alex's vehement objection.

"They're all *men*, Alanna! And not one is as interesting a person as you, for all their supposed brilliance," he growled. "I wish that you were down here with me. It's the kind of business trip that would be a second—or third or fourth—honeymoon if you were here."

"Alex . . ." Her warning was well taken and he relaxed.

"All right. No pressure." But he couldn't help a barb. "You can tell yourself *that*, tonight. Sleep well, love."

"You too, Alex."

It seemed a foregone conclusion that sleep would be uneven that night. And, indeed, it was. Alanna spent the evening sorting out the chaos of emotions that Alex's call had brought to the surface. She felt angry that he hadn't made a point of returning to keep their date, then scolded herself for her presumption. She had no right to demand anything from him, did she? But she was hurt—hurt that he had not demanded himself that his meetings be wound up to allow for his evening return. And, yes, she felt above all disappointed that she wouldn't see him until tomorrow, or perhaps the day after.

All in all, it did not bode well for sleep. How did one keep tension from the bedroom when one's body and senses and memory were filled to overflowing with frustration and unfulfilled desire? She lay in bed for ten minutes, trying to clear her mind, then jumped up in defeat. Twenty minutes later, she tried again; again, failure was immediate. When finally she did fall asleep it was well past midnight. She was not surprised, moreover, to find herself awake again at three.

Sitting in the living room with a glass of warm milk, she perversely hoped that Alex was having as much trouble as she was. Her mind's eye painted a picture of him in bed, the sheets thrown across his lean lines, the white linens a strong contrast to the dark sheen of his skin with the soft fur mat that had cushioned her blond tresses so deliciously. Her skin had begun to warm before she doggedly ousted the image.

Breathe deeply. Think of nothing. It was very hard work, this thinking of nothing! At length she returned to bed and, finally, to sleep. The morning, however, found her back to her rise-and-frown crankiness. Following Ellen's suggestion she did go for a swim at the pool. Then came a morning of leisure, reading the newspaper, sipping coffee, lounging in her warm fleece robe as she never had time to do on a work day. It was potentially a pleasant few hours. Why, then, did it drag?

The question was easily answered, though the answer was far from being to Alanna's satisfaction. It was Alex. Alex. Love. Marriage. Children. Forever . . .

Had Alex been right? What would her mother have said had she been able to see her only daughter now? Would she remind her daughter of the love and family that Alanna had sacrificed on the altar of corporate success? What *would* happen if she did agree to marry Alex? Would she be able to have it all—him, her career and a family? He had planted the seeds of doubt in her mind—a doubt that encompassed those ideas around which she had shaped her comings and goings for over ten years. Could she change her way of thinking?

In the end it came down to one basic factor. Love. Did she love Alex? If what she felt for him *was* love, change was worth considering. Though she believed firmly that love alone was not enough, without it there was no hope at all for a relationship with Alex. *He* was so sure, so very sure!

She spent the afternoon with her friends at the theater before moving on to a restaurant later. It was a welcome diversion from her deeply perplexing thoughts. As always she enjoyed their company, sharing the latest news with them, discussing broader issues as they came up. As she walked up to her apartment building shortly before eight she felt remarkably relaxed considering her lack of sleep the night before. But relaxation faded as her thoughts turned in anticipation to Alex's call.

As it happened she didn't have to wait for a call, for standing on her doorstep waiting for her was Alex himself.

Chapter Eight

*W*ithout even a "hello" or a "how are you" he moved toward her and a large and powerful pair of arms opened to swallow her up. Alanna melted into them. Though the air was chill it barely touched the warmth within and between them. For Alanna there was a sense of peace and contentment that had been missing in his absence. She felt as though she was, at last, home.

Alex's tan jacket was soft against her cheek, his hands insistently strong through her own dark wool coat. Their embrace seemed endlessly divine, until the intrusion of several of Alanna's fellow tenants broke the spell. Without a word Alex took her hand and led her inside the building to her apartment, silently taking the keys from her, unlocking the door and guiding her gently in. It was only when the door was firmly shut that he took her in his arms again.

There was a hunger in his kiss that was undeniable and matched with equal strength by Alanna. Her pulse raced through veins fast-warming with desire, the same desire that was reflected with such urgency in Alex's smoldering charcoal eyes when he finally pulled back to look at her. His gaze spoke the greeting; hers returned it. Then another message shot between them and Alanna realized just how much she had missed him. The deep and wondrous craving sprang from her core, propelling her toward him magnetically. There would be time for talk later. Now the need was for a more primal form of communication.

Gazes interlocked, they slipped their coats off and tossed them onto the living room couch. Her hand disappeared into his as he led her to her bedroom, then reappeared to allow her to undress herself. Heart pounding with growing excitement, she fumbled with buttons and zippers and stockings, all the while following the progress of the tall man before her.

Was it a mere thirty-six hours' absence that made him look this devastatingly handsome? Her shimmering brown-eyed gaze could not see enough of him. She followed as he wrenched off his tie and hastily disposed of his shirt, presenting his sturdy chest for her consideration as he kicked off the rest of his clothes.

By the time they stood revealed to one another her knees quivered helplessly. Without hesitation she went to him, unable to suppress a moan of pleasure when her skin came in contact with his. Her curves fitted against his lines with the perfection that had always been there, as though they had been molded specifically for each other.

Alex's hands sent ripples of ecstasy through Alanna's body. He touched her everywhere, head to toe, as he nudged her back onto the bed and her own fingertips, then lips, followed suit with a need that could not be quelled.

Within instants, Alex made her his and Alanna gloried in his possession. The heat of their passion built quickly to the boiling point, dampening their bodies in arousal until, with a simultaneous cry of ecstasy, they gave themselves over to an exaltation that encompassed both mind and body.

"I missed you," Alanna whispered breathlessly when finally the spasms of joy had subsided to allow for speech. Alex took a bit longer, his chest heaving as he slid off to lie by her side.

"I was hoping for something more far-reaching," he rasped thickly, his eye glittering his humor, "but I'll settle for that in the meanwhile. I missed you, too, Alanna."

On impulse she reached up to comb back the thick hair that had fallen onto his forehead. Her hand remained at the back of his head as she lay on her side to savor the sight of him.

His brief command took her by surprise. "Say it."

"W-what?"

"Your eyes did just now, but I'd like to hear you say it with your voice, so that you can hear it, too."

"*What?*"

"That you love me."

"I love you." It was soft and whispered, barely stirring the air around them, but Alanna *did* hear it and was nearly as surprised as Alex, whose dark eyes lit up with an exquisite happiness she could not have described had she tried later to do so.

His arms brought her against him once more as his lips moaned in her ear, "Ahhh. I've wanted to hear that so badly." Then he set her back an inch to study the still-startled expression that masked her features. "And when did you decide this?"

"I don't know." Still a whisper. Still barely audible. Still groping for understanding. "Just now, I guess."

"What finally clinched it? What brought about the great decision?"

She weighed the possibilities with a slow-growing composure. "I guess there had to be *some* explanation for the fact that we spend more time *in* bed than out."

One dark brow rose. "Could be pure lust . . . seems to me you did suggest that at one point."

"I *never* used the word 'lust,'" she chided, feeling in an increasingly good humor.

"Physical attraction, then. What about that?"

She shook her head determinedly. "By itself, not enough. I mean, do you realize that probably three-quarters of the time we've spent together has been in bed?"

"Chance circumstance, love," he offered, playing the devil's advocate. "After all, we did meet under very unusual conditions."

"Alex, why are you arguing with me this way? Aren't you pleased that your own argument finally got through to me? After all, you're the one who kept saying I wasn't a loose woman. Yet look at me. I've been totally wanton."

"You're in love." He grinned, satisfied. "Your body simply saw the truth before your mind was able to accept it. It's been *love* we've made all along."

Her sigh was exaggerated. "That's what I've been trying to tell you."

"Say it again," he ordered softly.

"I love you," she murmured against his chest, punctuating the vow with a kiss on his passion-damp skin. But a strong finger curved beneath her chin and angled her face up.

"Now, look me in the eye and say it."

His word was her command, in this instance, at least. "I love you."

"'I love you' . . . who?" He could have been speaking to a child.

"I love you, Alexander Knight." She indulgently played the game.

"Again!"

"I love you, Alex. I do."

"Ahhh, love. Why didn't you tell me sooner?" His accusation was soft, to be met by Alanna's incredulous rejoinder.

"I didn't *know!* How could I think to tell you?"

His grin of delight now spread from ear to ear. "It just tumbled out, didn't it—refused to remain inside any longer? *There's* the proof of its authenticity! It's the real thing! You love me," he sighed in what could only be termed relief.

Alanna was stunned anew by her confession. Struggling to assimilate its implications—for she did accept it as a fact—she buried her face against the warm solace of his neck, breathing in the manly tang that had so tantalized her in memory last night. Sensing her need for a moment's respite, Alex held her close. He felt neither a sense of triumph nor a desire to gloat at her long-awaited admission, simply the pleasure of know-ing that his sentiment was finally returned.

A strange shyness rendered her voice tremulous when finally she spoke. "How did those meetings go last night?" she asked, intentionally glossing over her heart-reaching discovery of moments earlier. Alex, however, would not.

"That's a fine question to ask on the heels of such an earth-shattering declaration!" he chided, snugly fitting his long arm around her back, stretching his lean fingers to hold the gentle swell of her breast.

Tilting her blond head back, she met his gaze. "I've surprised myself with all this, Alex. Give me time to take it all in, OK?"

Her beseeching gaze convinced him. "OK, love." He smiled indulgently, feeling infinitely patient as he pro-ceeded to fill her in on the meetings that had kept him from her yesterday. His bid had been successful; every-thing had worked out to his satisfaction. As soon as he could he shifted the conversation back to her.

Alanna would never know whether he had read that deep-hidden source of tension of which she, herself, was barely aware. But his question immediately brought it out. With Wednesday morning so close on the horizon there was Jake's board meeting to contend with.

"What's up at work this week?" Alex asked. "Any news on whether you'll be offered that opening?"

"Funny you should ask," she murmured against his chest, a noted absence of humor in her tone. "The board is meeting tomorrow morning. Jake plans to make the proposal then."

"It's definite?" His eyes lit up with an enthusiasm she wouldn't have expected. Most men would have been instantly wary of such a move by a woman. Not Alex. Perhaps that was one of the things she loved about him. . . .

Her headshake was half in response to that last thought as well as to Alex's prodding. "Not definite— until they vote. But if Jake proposes it, it's as good as done."

"Congratulations, love! I'm proud of you!" His lips touched her brow with their warmth; she felt as though she had received his blessing. Yet the matter was far from decided.

"Whoa! I'm not sure I'll accept the position even if it *is* offered to me!"

Alex looked at her as though she had suddenly become possessed by lunacy. "That's ridiculous! Whyever not?"

"Because," she answered firmly, "I can get just as much done from right where I am."

Alex drove to the heart of the matter. "It's the gossip that's discouraging you, isn't it?"

Her first impulse was to deny the allegation; then she admitted its truth to herself. It was the strength of her newfound love, and the faith it gave her, that enabled her to admit it to Alex. "I suppose so." Resting her chin on her hands, which in turn were resting on his chest, she drank in his self-assuredness. "It's not worth the fight."

What had been a softly spoken statement inspired one that was much more forceful. "Not worth it? Alanna, you've spent the past ten years waiting—

knowingly or not—for just this type of advancement. You're a fighter. If you have to you'll show them all!" His voice lowered. "Besides, once we're married—"

"I haven't agreed to marry you." Alanna's quiet voice stopped him cold. He looked at her in amazement.

"But you've just admitted that you love me. What more is needed?"

"What's needed," she took a deep breath, "is for me to be able to feel comfortable with the idea of marriage . . . and everything it entails."

For a long time Alex was quiet. His eyes studied her closely, then shifted to contemplate each strand of loose blond silk that had fallen free of its bonds in the frenzy of their lovemaking. His hands were still, though, and for the first time Alanna sensed a limit to his patience. His words confirmed as much.

"I can't wait forever, Alanna. You've dangled the carrot before my nose by just being you. Now, by saying you love me, you've brought it that much closer. I'm not made of stone." His tone was sober. "How long do you think you can toy with my emotions?"

She slid back against the sheets to look at the ceiling. Perhaps he was right. If she wasn't ready for total commitment was it fair to keep him in midair?

"I'm sorry," she whispered, turning on her side to face away from him, not quite mustering the will to leave the bed. "I don't mean to toy with you, Alex. It's just that . . . I didn't plan on this happening."

"Damn it!" he exploded, drawing her back to face him. "That's your problem—or one of them. In your work you can plan everything out to perfection. That's what makes you as efficient as you are. But in the world of human relationships you can't plot out a beginning and an end. You can't outline what's going to happen. You can't plot the whole thing out, then follow your plan to the letter. It just doesn't work that way!"

Alanna saw frustration in the depths of his charcoal gaze. She saw the faint lines of tension by the corners of his mouth. And she wanted desperately, desperately to give in. How simple it would be to agree to marry him! But the thought of marriage and a family sent tremors of apprehension through her. Until those tremors ceased she couldn't, in good faith, accept his proposal.

Sitting up on the bed, oblivious to her own nakedness, she faced him. The soft light from the dresser cast a golden glow on her hair, her shoulders, the gentle fullness of her breasts. It was a picture of innocent supplication she made as she began to talk quietly.

"I feel confused about so many things. What you've said is right. But it's difficult to change one's way of thinking overnight." She averted her eyes. "I never thought I'd say I loved you, but I have. Doesn't that give you hope?" A crooked smiled played at her lips.

Alex sat up to join her. "Hope can only take me so far. I want you for my wife. I won't rest until you're mine." There was a grim set to his lips that vouched for his determination. For an instant Alanna also wondered whether there was a touch of insecurity in this man who presented the image of strength and confidence at all times to the world. Was he afraid of *losing* her? Was that what was, in truth, behind his demand for marriage? Even as the thought of his possessiveness pleased her, she seized upon his words for diversion.

"So that's it, Alex Knight! You're using me!"

His ruggedly etched features formed a full-blown frown. "What on earth are you talking about?" he growled, his unusual lack of perception adding evidence of his vulnerability where Alanna was concerned. Her grin grew more mischievous.

"You can't *sleep* without me! Come on . . . confess! Did you sleep well last night?"

"Of course not!" The hint of a smile softened the straight line of his lips. "Did you?" he made his counteraccusation.

Her laugh was light and brief. "I certainly did," she looked toward the ceiling in recollection, "from roughly midnight till three, then from perhaps five till seven." When her gaze dropped to meet Alex's once more her humor had returned. "But, no, I didn't sleep through the night as I do with you," she confessed softly, meaningfully.

With a low groan Alex took her in his arms and hugged her tightly. "You will tonight, love. I promise you that!"

She did, as did he. By unspoken consent, they shelved all serious discussion in favor of an evening in bed talking of lighter things. Alex told Alanna of his childhood, of climbing Mt. Washington, of canoeing through the lakes of upstate Minnesota, of sailing on the Atlantic off the coast of Cape Cod. He talked of his college years, of receiving his master's degree, of joining the family business and having to fight for the respect of the men below him. He spoke of his brother and sisters, of his nieces and nephews, never once directly referring to the children of his own that he hoped to have one day.

In return for the wealth of information he freely offered Alanna related more of her own story, a less exciting one in her mind, but one by which Alex seemed fascinated. He encouraged her to talk of her parents, of the occasional good times they had had despite the legacy of bitterness which she had inherited. He coaxed her into telling him of her days at school, her friends, even her bouts of puppy love. And he drew from her a vivid picture of her life as a working woman and the pattern it had fallen into over the years. All the while he held her propped against him, his arms about her, her head against his shoulder.

When the intimacy of the interchange yielded to something more erotic Alanna grew aware once more of the love she felt for Alex. It was this love that emboldened her in her initial response to the masterful male hands that scorched her body. For the first time she was unafraid to face the extent of the arousal which only Alex could evoke in her. She felt free to exert herself as a woman, as a creature of passion. If there was a challenge now it was within her; she had to convince herself of the strength of her love by expressing it in Alex's arms.

The frenzied passion of earlier that evening had taken the edge off the awesome physical need they had for each other. This slow, more studied lovemaking was an exploration into depths they had skimmed but never probed. Soft words of love accompanied the gentle movements of arms and legs, lips and tongues. The heady wine of love drugged them, prolonging the moment of union with languorous strokings and tender caresses.

With his hands tracing the curves of her sides and hips Alanna found herself above Alex. Looking down at him she caught the golden highlights, cast by the lamp, which burnished the rich brown of his hair. Was he angel or devil, to have such magnificent power over her?

It didn't matter. For she gloried in that power, absorbing it in every cell of her being, then exerting it over him in turn. It was this last which astounded her even more, the strength of the force her woman's body could wield over the sturdy, muscled mass of masculinity which now held her weight.

With the grace of a swan she arched toward him. Her breasts touched his broad, hair-roughened chest, teasing electrically as her lips brushed his. The tip of her tongue circled his mouth, then ventured within its moist bounds when he moaned his pleasure. It was as though time itself had slowed to half speed. Haste was nonexistent. There was only the exquisite savoring of a physical arousal that warmed and heated and reached the near-boiling point in a drawn-out eternity of luscious touching and feeling.

When at last Alex groaned his urgent need, then echoed it with the strength of the hands that lifted her, Alanna was just as eager, taking him to her in a moment of mind-sweeping joy.

"I love you," she whispered between deep kisses.

"You've got me," he drawled as softly, letting her

take the lead, seeming to revel in the strength she possessed.

Tiny beads of sweat glistened on her body as the heat of passion burst from within. She felt herself the embodiment of all that was desirable. Alex's hands held her breasts as she arched her back in mindless delight. Her rosy nipples flamed at his touch, reacting as much to his faintly roughened fingertips as to the taut pull of the passion they shared.

Again they savored their joy with leisurely delight, their movements deliberate and thoroughly sensed. Alanna had never felt as rich, as filled with contentment, as when she held him and reveled in his virility. Adding to her happiness was the look of pure love that held Alex's gaze enmeshed with hers. He, too, had risen above the simply physical; he, too, understood and shared this spiritual elevation.

It was only the white-hot explosion of bliss that sent them at last to the spiraling heights from which they fell slowly, reluctantly, still wrapped in each other's arms. Alanna could no longer differentiate Alex's thudding heart from her own, his rasping breath from hers. They were one in every sense. As one they fell into the deep, deep sleep that had been denied them when they had been apart. As one they slept, fulfilled and satisfied, through the night and into the morning of the day that Alanna had been dreading.

The news came shortly before noon to Alanna at her desk. Within five minutes she found herself in the board room being introduced to the board members as the next Executive Vice-President of WallMar Enterprises. These were men whom she would come to know well in the future, as she would frequently be called to sit in on these board meetings. Some of them she knew already; others received her cordially, if guardedly. It was a reaction that would seem mild in comparison to that of some of her fellow workers.

Words were kept to a minimum, the traditional "congratulations" and "good luck"s filtering in throughout the afternoon. But the sidelong glances, the wary looks, the speculative gazes aimed her way said far more potent things. It was, once again, her usual adversary, Brian Winstead, who put it all into words.

"So it paid off, Alanna," he taunted, not quite daring to fully enter her office, but merely propping himself up in the threshold.

Alanna knew just what was coming. Prepared, she presented her most composed veneer. "Hard work always pays off, Brian," she replied with deliberate innocence.

But the leer Brian sent her way contained no innocence. "And it's meant a lot of nights filled with hard work, hasn't it? Boy, I'm really amazed; I never dreamed that Wallace had the stamina."

Had the venom been saved for her alone Alanna might have preserved her patience. Listening to Brian insult Jake Wallace, however, tried her beyond control. Rising from her desk, she held herself with confidence as she approached the door.

"I think you should come in, Brian. We've got something to discuss and I'd rather not have all of WallMar listening."

Surprised, Brian stepped across the threshold and Alanna slammed the door, her only sign of frustration. To all other appearances she was utterly composed, a remarkable feat considering the challenge before her.

"Privacy suits me well." He shrugged, sauntering toward a chair opposite the desk and sinking into it. His smugness irritated her beyond belief. Determined to squelch it, she perched on the edge of the desk to give herself the advantage of height.

Arms crossed before her, she spoke with quiet disdain. "I'm getting very tired of your accusations, Brian. Are you *that* jealous?"

"Of Wallace?"

"Of *me!*" she snapped.

He seemed momentarily startled by her force. He had never seen her so livid. "I'm not jealous of you or anyone else."

"No? Then why the problem each time I receive a promotion?" Her smile was deceptively benign.

"No problem. Just stating the facts."

"And the 'facts,' in your view, are . . . ?"

For the first time he grew defensive. "You know them. There's no need for me to repeat them."

"You've never been hesitant before," she goaded him, her gaze hardening quickly.

"I've never been specific—"

"You're right!" she interrupted, her temper flaring briefly before she forced herself to be calm. "You've always been vague, but very definitely suggestive. Now I'm asking for details. If you have accusations to make, back them up."

For long moments the battle was purely visual. Each

stared at the other, refusing to back down. The stalemate was broken only by Brian's absurd declaration. "Everyone around here knows how you've gotten to this office, Alanna." His gaze fell to the gentle curve of her breasts and it was all she could do to keep from showing the nausea she felt, but she held herself firmly.

"Go on." When his eyes continued to linger she added, "Say it."

Slowly Brian looked up. "It's common knowledge that you're having an affair with the boss."

Alanna's hands balled into fists behind her. "Is it? Common knowledge? Based on what proof?"

"Aw, come on. Look at you, Alanna." *He* did, once more, and she felt positively raped. "You've got all the right curves in the right places. What man in his right mind wouldn't take what's offered?"

Her eyes narrowed angrily. "And how do you know exactly what *has* been offered, Brian?"

He sat back. "You've gotten the promotions, haven't you? That speaks for itself."

"It does not!" she exploded, unable to contain her fury. "Has it ever occurred to you that I've *earned* those promotions through hard work," her forefinger jabbed at the desk, "in this office? No," she shook her head, "that would be too threatening for you, wouldn't it? It would imply that I legitimately earned a promotion over you. A sexist accusation is more your style; that way you can overlook any possible professional failing within yourself!"

Brian spoke evenly. "A psychoanalyst, too?"

"It's common sense, Brian," she spat out. *"Another* thing you seem to be lacking." She paused to steady her breathing and lower her voice. "I've been willing to put up with your sly little hints in the past because they're so absurd that they're not worth bothering about. But when you came out and mentioned Jake Wallace's name just now you went too far."

"If the shoe fits . . ."

In that instant Alanna realized she would never get anywhere with Brian Winstead. Perhaps that was why she'd never said anything before, intuitively sensing the futility of it. Now he was simply an outlet for the tension that had built up over this latest promotion.

Straightening, she slowly rounded the desk, tempering her annoyance to ponder the next step. When she reached her chair she slid fluidly into it, leaned back and feigned utter calm. Through it all Brian sat with a maddeningly impassive expression on his face. He didn't even blink when she began to talk quietly.

"I have three things to say to you." Her gaze was filled with an anger clearly held back at some cost. "First, I don't want to hear anything else from you on this matter unless you plan to produce concrete proof of your accusations. Second, I don't ever again want to hear Jake Wallace's name muddied by your tongue. He's worked too hard, too honestly and too respectably to build WallMar Enterprises. He doesn't deserve your filth." She inhaled sharply. "And finally, if I *do* catch wind of anything further, you can very probably fear for your job. Despite what your ego might lead you to believe, you are *not* irreplaceable."

"Is that a threat?" Brian sat forward for the first time, more indignant than worried.

But Alanna was not about to give him the upper

hand. She, too, sat forward, mirroring his movement. "It's a promise!"

"And you'd swing your weight with Wallace to see it through." It was not so much a question as a statement, verging on the very slander which had prompted their present confrontation. Again Alanna marvelled at his gall.

"Let's get this clear, Brian. Regardless of how you believe I got here, I am now the Executive Vice-President of WallMar. I won't need to swing *any* weight to send you packing. Based on job performance alone your position has been questionable at times. It's on the record, entered by hands other than mine. But you are familiar with the company and, when you want to, you can be quite effective. If, however, that effectiveness is hampered by thwarted ambition you might do better to seek employment elsewhere. As it is," she ventured, feeling suddenly drained, "if you continue with these unfounded accusations your co-workers may just begin to realize what a jealous and petty mind you have."

The object of her scathing denunciation slowly unfolded himself from his chair as though determined to be the one to end the audience. He cocked his head arrogantly. "People *may* just believe me." And with that he walked to the door and left.

Alone, Alanna settled back in her chair, took several deep calming breaths and proceeded to stew. The confrontation with Brian was but one small aspect of the situation. Now the force of the whole problem came down on her. Should she have accepted the promotion? Why *had* she accepted it, given the very serious reservations she had? Hadn't these past few minutes made real what she had feared?

But Alex's parting words of that morning echoed in her ears, her only source of courage. As he had stood at her door preparing to leave he'd taken her shoulders and held her firmly before him.

"Now, listen, Alanna." His gray eyes had reached her soul. "I want you to take it."

"Take what?" She'd feigned ignorance, preferring to bask in the pleasure she'd found in his arms such a short while earlier.

"The promotion, damn it!" he had growled impatiently. "You're more than capable of doing the work and you owe it to yourself to have the title."

She had shaken her head then, blond tangles falling about her shoulders. "I don't know. . . ."

But his voice had lowered in the tone of challenge she recalled from that very first encounter she'd had with this man she now loved. "Can't stand the heat? Fire too bright? You can always retire, give it all up, become a full-time homemaker. . . ."

His point had been well-taken. Business had been her whole life until Alex had entered it such a short time before. The precise nature of their future as a couple was still an enigma; her future at WallMar Enterprises was more fully sketched out. She realized that it wasn't Alex's dare that had goaded her into accepting the promotion. Rather, it was his underlying message. She had entered the corporate world in large part for the challenge it offered; to shy away from that challenge now, even considering the sordid aspect of one part of the drama, would be to turn her back on everything for which she'd worked so long and hard.

When Jake appeared at her office door at six and insisted on buying her a celebration drink she was more than happy to leave her work for another day and focus on the positive nature of this promotion. Alex had planned to pick her up at her own apartment for dinner at eight, so she had the time to spend with Jake, to whom she owed so much.

"I only wish Elaine could be here," she mused wistfully after Jake had toasted her future with the champagne he'd ordered as they sat together in a lounge not far from the office.

Jake's eyes sparkled with pleasure. "She's waiting for us at home. Drinks are just the beginning. There's a full-course meal on the agenda!"

Alanna was touched and excited. "How sweet of her, Jake! But she shouldn't have gone to the trouble!" Then she realized that Alex would be waiting, also. How nice it would be to bring him along, to have him meet these two people who had been so wonderful to her over the past few years!

Her face must have told the entire story, for Jake responded, "Alex should be there by the time we arrive."

The soft brown pools of her eyes warmed with pleasure. "But how did you . . . ?"

"Elaine did all the arranging, Alanna." He brushed the details away with the gentle sweep of one pudgy hand. "You'll have to ask her. You *were* planning to see him tonight, weren't you?"

"You know I was." Her answer held her smiling

resignation. "You're a pretty sharp fellow, Jake. Have I ever told you that before?"

"Save it for *him,* dear." The older man beamed at her. "He'll need all the bolstering he can get what with the fame you're finding!"

Alanna's blush was unbidden. "Alex Knight isn't about to be threatened by me. You'll see when you meet him."

What Jake and Elaine Wallace saw was a paragon of charm, wit and intelligence. Alex spent some time with Elaine before the others arrived, comfortably assisting her with the last minute dinner preparations. When Alanna and Jake walked through the front door it was Alex who nonchalantly wheeled a glowing Elaine from the kitchen, Alex who mixed the first round of drinks, Alex who was fully composed and utterly triumphant in his conquest of the Wallaces.

Much later that night Alanna hugged him especially hard for the genuine and forthright warmth that he had shown her friends. "Thanks, Alex," she murmured, burying her face against the strong column of his neck.

"For what?" His arms curved about her slender body reflexively as they stood in her living room.

Alanna tipped her blond head back to survey the gentleness of the features that seemed so perfectly to depict manliness. "For being so wonderful to them, with them. Elaine is often sensitive with new people, but she seemed totally at ease with you."

Silver sparkles shimmered in his eyes. "*You* should know about my way with women. . . ."

"But you were great with Jake, too!" she quickly went on. "I can't believe how freely he discussed

WallMar with you. He's usually more guarded with a potential competitor."

One dark brow arched. "Perhaps he sees me as a future in-law of sorts." His gaze narrowed. "You know, I couldn't help but notice how he looked at you. He does see you as a daughter. And unless I'm way off base, I think he'd like to see you married."

Alanna scoffed at the suggestion though she knew it to be fact. "If that was the case why would he just have had me promoted?"

"Perhaps he agrees with me that you can do the job whether or not you're married."

Sensing that they were on the verge of a discussion she was still unready to tackle, Alanna moved out of Alex's arms and crossed the room to stand by the sofa. Her voice was very soft. "Please don't hassle me, Alex. I've had enough tension today without this. I already have too many second thoughts about taking the job; what I really need is your support." At the instant she said it she knew it to be the truth. Had Alex not been part of her life now she wondered whether she would have had the courage to accept the promotion she knew was so controversial among her co-workers. It had been this time with him that she had looked forward to all day; these moments made everything else worthwhile.

Alex's long strides brought him to her in an instant. His arms were iron bands, surging with strength as he held her. "Have I told you how proud I am of you?" he whispered, the warmth of his breath flowing over the skin of her cheek. "I have to confess, it was very easy to like Jake and Elaine, seeing how much they obviously adore you."

Touched by his words, she could only cling to him. This was the man she loved; his praise meant the world to her. It put things in perspective, made things special. *He* made things special when he was with her. What would she ever do if she lost him?

Her throat constricted around a half gasp as she understood, at last and with a sudden clarity, the full meaning of fear. It had been hard enough to assimilate the fact that she loved him. This new information—that she did, indeed, want him to be part of her life on a permanent basis—shocked her even more. Shocked her, frightened her, disconcerted her . . . and left her at a loss for words.

As it happened there was no need for words at that moment, for Alex's firm lips took possession of her softer ones and expressed his pride in her in a far more sensual way than mere words had been able to do. And, as always, she was helpless against the heady assault, finding herself caught up with lightning speed in the swirl of desire. All thoughts of the future were forgotten in the mind-dazing heat of the moment. For Alanna, this—rather than the promotion she'd received that morning—was what she'd been waiting for. It brought her more spontaneous excitement, more instant gratification, than anything she had ever known. And she gave to it with every atom of her being, offering her own body, burning now with desire, for Alex's adoration. It was an exalted lovemaking they shared, one that was destined to repeat itself at random intervals throughout the night.

Morning brought the unpleasant necessity that Alex leave. He was off to the West Coast for three days.

"Must you?" she protested on impulse, well before she realized that she had no right to rebel.

Alex had pulled on his shirt; his tie hung loosely around his neck. He would go home to change, then head for the airport. "I'm afraid I've got to. It's Joey. Several times a year I have to visit the California offices and give him the pat on the back *he* needs."

"This is Tuesday; when will you be back?"

"I've got meetings scheduled through Thursday. There's a bare chance I may make it back by Friday noon, but I doubt it. What say I pick you up from work on Friday?"

Trying to cope with the pervasive sense of loneliness that the prospect of three full days without Alex brought, she nodded. "That sounds fine." There was more she wanted to say, but she bit her lip. Did she have the right to sound possessive? Did she have the right to ask that he call from California?

"I'll call tonight." He read her mind, smiling tenderly down at her. "Keep your chin up at work, OK? Don't let them get to you."

Standing at the door beside him, she let her gaze linger on him, committing each manly feature, each powerful line to memory. "I'll try." With this image in her mind she might, indeed, have a chance.

Alex called that night, at three in the morning, Alanna's time. "Ellen would be very proud of us, you know," Alanna commented. "She said we should use each other to work out our problems. It helps—talking to you like this in the middle of the night."

The deep voice crackled sensuously over the cross-country wire. "I didn't wake you?"

"What do *you* think?"

He cleared his throat. "I was . . . kind of . . . hoping as much. . . ."

"Alex! Do you mean to say that you're *glad* I can't sleep?"

There was no hesitation in his voice, nor a drop of remorse. "Damned right, I am! Honestly, woman, if you could sleep as well without me as with me you wouldn't have *any* need of me at all!"

His words gave her food for thought as she lay awake after they had hung up. It occurred to her that for a man to want a woman who was as independent and self-sufficient as she was he had to truly love her. It was a mind-boggling thing to know that Alex loved her enough to be willing to accept her as an equal partner. Strange, she mused repeatedly, how her image of him had changed. When she had first met him he'd been the embodiment of the arrogant, domineering chauvinist with his impulsive proposal of marriage. Now she saw that her assessment of him had been wrong from the start. What she had interpreted as arrogance had been self-confidence; what she had interpreted as a drive for domination had been strength of character. And as for chauvinism—this man saw her as a modern woman and was willing to welcome her into his life as such.

In the final analysis Alanna realized that she was facing the greatest challenge of her life. Could she be a wife to Alex and mother to his children while still retaining her career? Could she be the complete, modern woman? Could she broaden her previous view of life to include love and family as well as work?

Half on impulse she phoned Ellen Henderson that

morning. Though she hadn't been in contact with the medical center or its staff psychologist since she and Alex had been sent home to "work things out," she sensed that Ellen might offer her insight, comfort or both. Their rapport had been good from the start. Even when Alanna and Alex had unintentionally messed up Ellen's study, the latter had been understanding. It was this very understanding on which Alanna now counted.

"How are you, Alanna?" Ellen remembered her instantly.

"Fine. Uh, not so fine. That's why I'm calling." She felt the same swell of helplessness and awkwardness seeking help that she'd felt when she'd first signed up for the IAT study.

"Problems sleeping again?"

"No. . . . Yes. . . . Well, indirectly. But that's not why I'm calling."

"It's Alex."

"And I can hear your smile over the phone." Yes, the rapport was still there.

Ellen chuckled. "He's quite a man! What's he up to now?"

"Right now he's out of town. I . . . I wondered if we could . . . talk."

There was a slight pause. "I sense that this isn't a counselor-client type of talk."

Alanna smiled softly as she twisted the telephone cord around her finger. "Not really. I was hoping for something on the line of friend-friend."

This time Ellen didn't hesitate. "How about lunch tomorrow? Here? That'll give us more time."

Accordingly, the next day at one, Alanna met Ellen at her office and together they made their way to the hospital cafeteria. It was only when they'd settled themselves in a quiet corner that Ellen broached the subject of Alex.

"Now, tell me about him. You're still seeing him, aren't you?"

"Oh, yes." Alanna picked at her chef salad. "We're still going strong. That's part of the trouble."

"How so?" Ellen grinned. "Is he still running on about love and marriage?"

"He's serious!"

"And you?" The psychologist sampled her hamburger as she studied Alanna's frown.

"I'm afraid to say that he's emerged victorious. I'm hooked."

Ellen's enthusiasm was spontaneous. "That's great, Alanna! The two of you couldn't be more perfectly matched! This is a new twist in the phenomenon of the sleep lab! But you said 'afraid.' What's the catch?"

Alanna's expression was close to melancholy. "The catch is . . . marriage."

It was Ellen's turn to frown, but in puzzlement. "He wants it. He told me as much."

"*I* don't."

"Ahhh, that's right. I remember your reaction that day in my office when Alex mentioned the possibility of marriage. But you weren't sure you loved him then. You are now?"

"Yes." It was evident in every fiber of her being.

"Yet you're still against marriage."

"Uh-huh." Alanna gathered her thoughts. "I've

tried to explain it all to Alex. He listens and I think he understands. It's *me* who's the most confused. That's why I wanted to talk with you. You see, I've spent my entire adult life building my career." Briefly she sketched the picture of her childhood and parents that she'd painted in far greater color and depth for Alex. "I ruled out the prospect of marriage and family a long time ago," she concluded. "Suddenly I'm wondering if I was right. I can't decide."

Ellen smiled in sympathy. "Whether it would work *and* be compatible with your career?"

"Exactly. How do *you* do it, Ellen? I remember you saying that your husband is a doctor here. How do you manage it all?" She speared a ripe cherry tomato in frustration as she awaited Ellen's answer.

Her companion was cautious. "You have to understand that we have no children yet. That simplifies things for the time being."

"Do you plan to have children?" Alanna asked on impulse, then caught herself. "I'm sorry. That was none of my business."

"No, no. It's a perfectly legitimate question. And timely. We've discussed it at length. You see, Sandy is, in many ways, very traditional."

Alanna couldn't help but be skeptical. "But you said you had a modern marriage—no ring, no name switch, no title."

"We do. Fortunately Sandy is open to change and loves me enough to realize that I need my work. There's still that part of him, though, that would like me at home, raising his brood, waiting for him." She paused. "Sound familiar?"

Alanna nodded ruefully. "My parents. But . . . Sandy *does* accept your career?"

"He does. We compromise. I make a point to do it big at home one day a week—you know, warm fire waiting, fancy dinner, total attention focussed on him. That seems to satisfy his need. And, to be truthful, I really enjoy it because it does mean so much to him. In turn he shares everything with me on the other days. He's very proud of my work."

"He *should* be! Is there . . . jealousy?"

"Between Sandy and me?" Ellen laughed in relief. "Thank goodness, no! We may both work here, but our fields are as different as night and day. And besides, Sandy and I are both relatively self-confident people. As are you and Alex." The last was added more pointedly as Ellen brought the discussion back to Alanna and her immediate problem.

"Yes, I suppose Alex and I *are* fairly secure. I can't imagine there being jealousy between us. But I do worry about being a successful wife and mother."

Ellen nibbled on a pickle. "The role has changed drastically in recent years, Alanna. Actually, the full-time wife at home is, in many cases, a luxury that only the well-to-do can afford. In your case you'd work because you wanted to. I'm sure Alex accepts that."

"He does." Alanna defended him quickly. "It's *me* who can't accept it, I guess. I imagine I'll feel this horrible guilt all the time. I should be doing this or I should be doing that. Do you ever feel guilty while you're at work about all of those other things that aren't getting done?"

"Sure I do." Ellen smiled.

"Doesn't it get you down?"

"Only until I share it with Sandy. He understands me . . . and my needs. We've always been able to reach solutions together." She hesitated, then frowned. "Lately I've been going through that guilt trip about kids. I want them . . . I don't want them. But I'm not getting any younger, as they say."

"What will you do?"

The dark-haired woman raised her eyes speculatively. "I've decided to leave things up to fate, for starters. What will be from here on will be."

"And if you do become pregnant, how will you handle it?"

"As we've worked it out in our minds, I'll work right through the pregnancy, then see my private patients from our place until I feel comfortable returning to the hospital." She shrugged. "For all I know I may even find private practice to my liking."

Alanna's eyes held admiration. "You sound very positive about the whole thing, Ellen. I'm envious."

"Don't give me too much credit yet." Ellen smiled wryly. "To be blunt, I'm terrified. For one thing, our income will be sharply reduced when I stop working. And then, things could backfire. If I do get pregnant I could be too exhausted to work until the last month or the baby could be a toughie and prevent me from getting back to work afterward. I could have trouble getting sitters or find myself without enough patients to cover the cost. The list goes on and on."

"But you're willing to take the risk?"

"I am."

"May I ask why?"

"It's very simple. I *do* want children. Somehow we'll work something out regarding my career. Regarding motherhood, it's either now or never. With any luck it'll be now."

Alanna dropped her gaze to focus absently on the last of her lunch. If she had expected black-and-white directives from Ellen Henderson she had misjudged the situation. There were no absolutes. It was all relative, all a matter of compromise.

"Have I helped you out at all, Alanna?" The psychologist, now her friend, broke into her silent meanderings.

Alanna looked up, startled. "Oh, yes! You have, Ellen! If nothing else you've suggested that I'm not the only one to fear torn loyalties. It's reassuring to know that it's not just my own private paranoia."

"What I'm also saying," Ellen added gently, "is that it's not your problem alone. It's for you and Alex to work out *together*. I'm sure you will."

Alanna was not quite as sure. The only thing she *was* sure about was how lonely she was without Alex. He was constantly in her thoughts. Perhaps it was fortunate that he should occupy so much of her mind for otherwise she would have surely brooded about the tension at the office. In her most optimistic dreams she had hoped that, once it was definite, the promotion would simply be accepted as fact. No so among her male associates. Her confrontation with Brian notwithstanding, few words were spoken on the matter. But the strain of the situation grew greater as the week went on. Men who had previously chatted amiably with her now were aloof. Those who worked closely with her on the various projects under her jurisdiction were similarly distant. Cordial . . . but distant. It was as though Brian had been right; people *had* believed him. Alanna had, indeed, taken a step up—up and away from the confidence of the men with whom she would have to work successfully if her career itself was to be successful.

As fate would have it, it was Alex who, appearing in person at her office late Friday afternoon, presented both the best and the worst of her life to date. The best was himself; a sight for love-starved eyes, he was stunningly handsome in his three-piece pin-striped suit, the shadow of a beard on his jaw. The worst, however, was foreshadowed by the look of barely bridled anger in his gaze as he threw down the first edition of the evening paper, opened to the business section and a close-up photo of Jake and herself sharing drinks at the lounge four days before.

"One Woman's Formula for Corporate Success," the headline read, its implication all too clear in conjunction with the picture. Instinct outlined the copy for her; Alex's anger elaborated on it. Tossing her glasses atop the newsprint, she closed her eyes in defeat. No wonder people had been so wary of her all day.

Chapter Nine

$\mathcal{W}$e'll sue!" Alex yelled, pacing the floor of her office as though he personally had been the subject of the slanderous passage Alanna had finally forced herself to read. It occurred to her that she had never seen him so angry.

"We won't sue," she contradicted him softly and distractedly. "It would only make a larger issue out of this entire farce." Her jaw tensed in frustration. "Someone fed this reporter her information. It could have been any one of the men who might have wanted advancement here. But I can't start pointing fingers." She looked up at Alex helplessly. "There are too many possibilities and no proof."

The eyes that speared her were dark and stormy. In the instant Alanna prayed that she might never have to face this man's wrath; it was truly awesome.

"Well, you can't just sit and let this type of thing go unchallenged, Alanna!" he seethed, slapping the newspaper back onto her desk. "There has to be a limit to journalistic freedom. You *do* have a case for libel."

Sighing, she looked down at the article, bristling freshly. "Of course, I do. But be practical. If I go to court it will cost a pretty penny. And realistically, if I go to court someone will try to tear apart my character even *more!*"

She was right. Even Alex, pausing in his anger to ponder her claim, had to reluctantly agree. But his mind ran quickly ahead. "Make a counterstatement."

"A *what?*" Her tone of voice was infinitely weary, just barely curious.

"A counterstatement." Alex had calmed down as a sensible course of action formulated itself in his mind. "If it were me," he eyed her with gentle accusation, "I'd call an immediate press conference—"

"It's *not* you—" she interrupted, only to be interrupted in turn.

His smile was meager and rueful. "I know. And since you won't put up with *that* the next best thing would be for you to submit a statement to the paper contradicting this woman's claims and presenting your own viewpoint. It might actually be," he grinned, "good PR for you."

"Alex! Publicity is the *last* thing on my mind. It's not what I need or want!"

"But a low-key statement, love?" he coaxed her, growing steadily more composed.

Alanna was skeptical. "You really think that would be better than simply ignoring the whole thing?"

"You could ignore it." He shrugged. "But somehow I always saw you as a more aggressive type."

There was the challenge once more. Pulling herself

up straighter in her chair, she nodded. "A counterstatement it will be, then."

A counterstatement it was, written jointly by Alex and Alanna and submitted to the newspaper only after a meeting with Jake, two of the members of the board of directors and the public relations specialist on Jake's staff. It was a simply worded piece, disclaiming the content of the earlier article as being pure fabrication. It enumerated Alanna's professional qualifications, her achievements at WallMar Enterprises and listed the projects now in the works because of her initiative. When it appeared in the paper there was an atmosphere of dignity about it. Its straightforward presentation of the facts seemed unimpeachable.

Implicit in the statement was a denunciation of the woman's source, most probably one of the men at WallMar, whose being passed over for promotion had prompted such vindictiveness. The subtle force of Alanna's words was silently aimed at Brian Winstead. She considered him the most obvious suspect, though she could openly say nothing to that effect.

The counterstatement, however, did not appear in the paper until Monday morning. In the interim Alex was a godsend. He devoted his entire weekend to Alanna, accompanying her as she did each of her usual chores, buoying her up.

He was a gentle and unobtrusively helpful presence in getting Elaine Wallace to and from the beauty shop. He manned the supermarket cart while Alanna shopped, endearingly tossing an extra ten dollars worth of his favorite foods into the pile. He even came to the rescue at the swimming pool when one of the girls, a tiny ten-year-old, appeared with a knee-to-toe cast on her leg and an accompanying heartbroken look on her face. Alex took over her care, sitting in the stands beside her, talking steadily, coaxing smile after smile from the child until the meet was over, at which time he led her outside and kept her company until her older sister was dressed and their mother had claimed them.

Sunday was a quieter day. They slept late, brunched out, walked along the waterfront for hours talking and took in an early movie before returning to her apartment. Through it all, however, despite Alex's encouragement, Alanna was shadowed by thought of the paper and the statement that would be appearing on Monday. Hers was a strong piece, she knew, but, unfortunately, she had been correct in an earlier fear. People would believe what they wanted to believe.

When Monday morning arrived and she dutifully appeared at WallMar with her head held high she met a world of doubting minds and wary eyes. If anything she found an increase in the unease among the men with whom she had to deal. She was deeply discouraged. Perhaps the greatest source of her discomfort lay in the fact that not one of her co-workers made even the slightest reference to the newspaper article—not even in passing. Surely, there would be *some* supportive comment. . . .

The week passed on leaden feet, seeming to be the longest of Alanna's life. Had it not been for the nightly comfort of Alex and the daily support of Jake she might have thrown in the towel right then.

Only subtle glances and strained interchanges gave proof of the feeling that seemed to run high against her within the corporation. To her dismay, even the other female faces on the payroll eyed her distrustfully, apparently choosing to believe the gossip rather than give her the benefit of the doubt.

Brian Winstead, historically her most vocal opponent, said nothing. She finally decided that either her personal "promise" to him had hit its mark or it was he who had spread the gossip to the papers in search of revenge and so was now sated. But as she had told Alex so firmly when the story had first broken, she had no proof. To accuse Brian blindly would be as wrong as his having made such unsubstantiated claims in the first place.

To further disturb her peace of mind was the growing sense of love she felt for Alex. As the days passed she came to depend on him—on his being there with her in the evenings, at night, when she awoke in the morning. They spent nearly every free moment together, primarily at Alex's suggestion, though she would have been distraught had he not done so. It was a tug-of-war, this wanting to be constantly with him yet fighting the urge to depend on him, and it continued unendingly.

For the first time, moreover, the physical was secondary to the emotional in their relationship. The intense attraction was there, as it always had been, as it always would be. But they now found different ways to express their love. There was more talking, more quiet companionship. During this time of tension for Alanna Alex came through with a wealth of understanding and encouragement. He patiently drew from her a retelling of the highs and lows of each day, dealing with both in a thoughtful and caring manner.

Their lovemaking was gentler, with none of the frenzied hunger of earlier encounters. It was as though each sensed the other's depth of feeling and was satisfied by that alone. They spent more than one night simply lying together, talking, savoring the closeness until sleep claimed them. And there was the quiet pleasure of waking together after an undisturbed sleep to greet the new day.

That she loved him Alanna now accepted fully. That she needed him was a different matter. She fought this reality for as long as she could, finally yielding by the end of the week. What she would have done without his strength she did not know. Without her even realizing it, Alex had insinuated himself into her life, had made himself a vital part of it. What he had originally done in the physical realm—building up her need for him until she was clearly addicted—he now did emotionally. He was always there and she grew to depend on him. She needed him. Yet she couldn't quite get herself to tell him that . . . yet.

There was still that matter of long-range commitment. To confess to Alex the true extent of her love for him would only give fodder for his argument in favor of marriage. So far he had kept his word about giving her time, easing the pressure he might otherwise have exerted in that direction. Quite subconsciously she needed to hold something back—a little something of herself, kept in reserve, preventing total surrender. It was a final connection to her past dreams, dreams that, though Alex's intrusion had rendered them inferior to the new pictures he painted of her future, she was not yet ready to give up entirely. She had spent too long building those old dreams; she still needed time to accept their obsolescence.

As she stood at a crossroads in her life she felt herself pulled in all directions at once. On one side were WallMar and the powerful position of Executive Vice-President, but with suspicion and innuendo shadowing her every move. Then there were Alex and her love for him, growing stronger day and night. And there were freedom and independence and self-sufficiency, long fought for and now threatened by the very love which welled within. For she knew that her life would be empty without Alex. Yet how long would he wait? How long would he be content to satisfy her need for love and companionship and comfort without her satisfying his need for a wife?

With the advent of the weekend her thoughts came full circle. Once more she found herself pondering what her mother might have said or done given the present situation. Once more she found herself wondering whether her parents had ever shared the heights of passion which she and Alex scaled night after night. Perhaps her mother's bitterness had been, in part, caused by a deep, deep love that was never quite returned. Perhaps . . . perhaps . . . perhaps . . . but Alanna would never know. Therein lay the greatest frustration.

It was with thoughts of her own past fresh in her mind that Alanna found herself, on Saturday evening, dressed in a soft blue sheath and navy heels, her blond hair brushed to a shine and hanging beyond her shoulders, en route to dinner with Alex's parents.

"But you said we were going out for dinner to a special place, just the two of us!" she protested when Alex informed her of the change of plans.

"Uh-uh," he chided her with half-hidden amusement. "I never said we'd be alone. You must have assumed that. But I do think that my home is a special place. . . ."

"That's not the point! You could have warned me! I'm not psyched up for this. Your *family*, Alex—why didn't you *tell* me?"

The gray Porsche purred smoothly away from the city, headed toward the suburban countryside in which Alex had grown up. "Relax, love. Where's that cool I always admire? That crystal-clear poise? That mirror-smooth composure?" The corners of his firm lips twitched. "If I didn't know you better I'd say you were scared to death!"

"You bet I am!" she agreed readily. She *was* scared and she wasn't quite sure why. Was it her own insecurity showing? Did she actually fear that Alex's parents might not like her? Resorting to humor to quell her nerves, she quipped lightly, "In fact, I'd like nothing better than to be in jeans and a shirt, back at my place. I'd cook you anything your stubborn little heart desired . . ."

His deep voice lilted in gentle harmony. "But you're here, with me, on the way to the country."

She sighed. "Yes."

He cast her a sidelong glance as she slowly gathered

her composure. "And you'll come with me and meet my family."

"Yes." Why she was so pliant to his wishes she wasn't sure, until he filled in the blank himself.

"Because you love me so much."

His deep growl ignited ripples of now-familiar longing within her. When she reached for his hand he offered it. "Yes, I do love you." She smiled, finding it impossible to stay angry at him for long. "But you've got to do something about these seats!"

"What's wrong with the seats? I'll have you know that this Porsche is a collector's item."

Alanna retaliated with a playful scowl. "The collectors can have it! Bucket seats are for the birds!"

The deep and steady surge of the motor was as smooth in its power as the man behind the wheel when he let out a low, long chuckle. "I won't argue with you there. But it may be for the best. If we *ever* hope to get to my parents' house . . ."

Get there they did. The sleek Porsche easily rounded the circular drive, then came to a halt before the tall, white-columned Georgian colonial. Well lit in the darkness, the house offered a warm welcome that served to alleviate the chill of apprehension Alanna felt. How much simpler it had been, she mused, to stand before that board of directors last week. How much simpler it had been even to face the antagonism of those more vehement of her co-workers. Alex was right; where had her cool sophistication suddenly gone? Yet all the self-chiding in the world could not quell the nervousness she felt. Alex's supportive hand as he led her from the car past a wealth of lush landscaping toward the front door helped—as did the warm welcome offered by Alex's father. His stature was grand, though more mature and mellowed than his son's; his features were likewise well aged, as a fine wine coming into its own. Even his hair, rich and full, but sporting dashing shots of gray where Alex's strands of gold were now, spoke of what the son might look like in twenty years' time.

"Alanna," Alex's voice interrupted her analysis, "I'd like you to meet my father, Benjamin Knight. Dad, this is Alanna Evans."

The strong hand that came out to clasp hers and draw her into the house bore the same brand of dignity that had been passed on to Alex. Alanna found herself quickly responsive to the self-confidence and sure manner of her host.

"Alanna," the older man spoke in a voice somewhat lower and a touch more raspy than that of his son, "this is a pleasure. Alexander seems to be quite smitten. At first glance I can see why!"

"Alexander" seemed not in the least embarrassed by his father's blatant reference to the state of his heart. Rather, the grin he showered on her as she looked back at him one final time before being ushered more deeply into the spacious front hall was nearly reckless.

"Alexander," she replied coyly to his father, "seems easily smitten at first glance, as well!" The gentleness of her tone and the softness of her brown-eyed gaze guaranteed her statement the good humor she had intended. Benjamin Knight's appreciative smile accepted it in a like manner.

"Come." He helped her off with her coat, then guided her toward the living room where he deftly and graciously introduced his wife, Adele, and Alex's sister and brother-in-law, Amanda and Paul Winters. Alex's own surprise at the latter couple's presence was genuine enough to spare him Alanna's later wrath. And, in truth, once in the clutches of Benjamin Knight, guardian extraordinaire, she had begun to feel surprisingly comfortable.

Alex's mother was equally warm, if perhaps a bit more guarded at the start, as was his sister. Each in turn echoed the news that Alex had spoken highly of her and congratulated her on her new position at WallMar Enterprises. Ribbons of invisible tension slithered about in Alanna's stomach, only slightly eased by the glass of wine that Alex placed in her hand. Well aware that she was, in a way, on trial, Alanna willed herself to maintain a state of composure.

"It's quite an achievement," Adele Knight complimented her, "for a woman your age to become an Executive Vice-President in an organization such as WallMar Enterprises."

Measuring her words, Alanna responded gently. "I consider myself to have been very, very fortunate. I was at the right place at the right time. When I first became associated with WallMar there was a distinct void where the type of projects I wanted to do should have been. Jake Wallace had an open mind and was willing to loosen the purse strings to give my ideas a chance."

It was Amanda, who appeared to be a year or two older than Alex and was a replica of the mother, who followed up. Her knowledge of the field startled Alanna. "I particularly appreciated WallMar's entrance into educational slide production. Since Paul is an educator we've seen your ideas serving some very practical purposes."

Alanna turned instinctively toward the man who sat propped against the arm of his wife's chair. "You're in education?"

The pleasant-looking man nodded. "When I decided to marry Amanda I had a choice." His hazel eyes twinkled through his wire-rimmed spectacles, foretelling amusement to come. Amanda felt immediately drawn to him, a onetime outsider who now seemed very comfortable amidst the Knights. His voice was as soothing as his manner. "I knew that I could either enter the fold and go into business or steer a course into a different field entirely. I had been a teacher; now I'm a high school principal. I find the work very exciting."

"And his school system uses WallMar's slide kits constantly," Benjamin Knight interjected. "Tell me, Alanna, has your marketing effort extended across the entire country? At last report I heard that you still had the western states to conquer."

"You're right." Alanna grinned, feeling more and more relaxed. "I suppose it gives us something to work toward."

Other questions about her work followed. Though Alex sat beside her on the beautiful French Provincial sofa, one of several such pieces setting the tone of this elegant room, he let her pave her own way, his evident confidence in her unblemished by her moments of hesitancy in the car.

The conversation flowed gently from business to theater; then Adele Knight disappeared, only to return moments later with a large platter of hot hors d'oeuvres from the kitchen.

"Mother's favorite recipe." Amanda coaxed Alanna to try the delicate zucchini tarts which, surrounded by a variety of other choices, were indeed delicious. But her compliments had to be put off until later; they fell victim to the avid discussion that had erupted between the men regarding the quality of present-day live theater in light of the moving picture industry. Within moments the women, as well, had expressed their opinions. To her astonishment Alanna found herself joining in quite unself-consciously.

It was a harbinger of what was to come, an evening of stimulating conversation, fine food and wine. At one point Alanna looked down into the swirl of wine in her glass. Momentary guilt washed over her as she remembered Ellen Henderson's instructions, now disregarded. But then, she smiled to herself with satisfaction, sleep would not be a problem this night. Her love-warmed gaze lifted to meet that of Alex, who sat by her side at the beautiful dinner table, mirroring her thoughts exactly and betraying them with a depth of desire in his eyes that brought a blush of embarrassment to Alanna's cheeks. His thigh seemed suddenly that much closer to hers; his hand moved beneath the table to sear through her dress to her leg. His lips moved, silently but clearly outlining the words "I love you."

Of necessity their outward attention turned back to the others, yet a special awareness filtered through the air between them, charging it with the force of the attraction that always existed for them. Though in company they were removed, secure in their own world within a world with the knowledge of a passion that would surely follow later.

What followed more immediately were after-dinner drinks, again in the living room, and a few moments of conversation alone with Alex's mother and sister while the men saw to some personal matter in the den.

For a fleeting instant, as the men disappeared, Alanna felt a return of trepidation, particularly when Adele Knight brought up the one topic that had nagged at the back of Alanna's consciousness all evening.

"I thought you handled that article very well," the older woman said softly, obviously feeling a need to say something on the subject. "Your statement was a strong one. I'm glad you decided to answer her."

Alanna regarded Alex's mother with respect and shrugged. "I have to confess that I might have tried to ignore her had Alex not prodded me. He wanted me to do something even *more* vocal."

"*I* would have called a press conference," Amanda exclaimed with the same feistiness that seemed so much a part of Alex's character, as well.

Alanna couldn't help but laugh. "That's precisely what Alex said! You must all think alike!"

"We're fighters." Amanda returned the grin as her thought was promptly seconded by her mother.

"Each in our own way. Alex certainly is." Was there a hidden meaning in what she said? "When he sets his heart on something he rarely lets it get away from him."

Later, as Alanna and Alex drove back toward the city, Alanna recalled the very first day she had met him. He had announced then that he would marry her. Would he? He'd actually gotten her to the point of declaring her love for him. Would an agreement of marriage be next? Despite all her lingering doubts the thought held none of the instant horror it might have such a short time ago. Particularly since seeing Alex's family. . . .

"Penny for your thoughts?" The deep voice broke into her reflection. His hand touched hers; his fingers closed around hers. His self-assuredness flowed through to her. She had no way of knowing of the strength he derived from *her* presence.

"I was thinking of your family. They're lovely, Alex."

"You had doubts?" In the dark of night, with only the intermittent flare of oncoming headlights to illumine his face, she could only hear his smile. There was nothing smug in it.

"I'm afraid," she blushed, grateful that her color would be hidden in the darkness, "that I had formed a picture of them even before I knew I was to meet them."

"Tell me," he coaxed softly.

"They were to be worldly and attractive, attended by a bevy of servants, concerned principally with money matters and very distrustful of, even condescending toward, me."

"And now . . . ?"

"As I said, they *are* lovely. They brought me right into their world, discussing things that, even if I wasn't informed, I'd find interesting. I think your mother, perhaps your sister, too, wasn't quite sure at first about this woman you'd brought home, but they both turned out to be perfectly delightful."

Alanna caught Alex's nod as a car passed. His features mesmerized her for that moment—the chiseled power of his lips, his nose, his forehead. When he smiled the white of his teeth gleamed in the dark. "They liked you."

"How could you tell?" She felt suddenly anxious, realizing that she did want them to like her.

"In the first place," there was undeniable humor in his tone, "my father left you alone with my mother. He doesn't always do that."

"Come on, Alex. Your mother strikes me as a very lovely lady."

"Not where her oldest son is concerned, love. She's known to be very possessive, sometimes too tough. My father quickly sensed both that you could hold your own with my mother *and* that she could easily warm to you."

If what he'd said was true he'd given her quite a compliment. "And in the second place?"

"In the second place," he cleared his throat, "he invited you for a return visit."

Alanna cocked her head in puzzlement. "But that was simply out of courtesy. Any host would have said the same!"

"Not Benjamin Knight. He's reached the stage in life where he only says what he means. Oh, he's never been crude, never insulting. He simply omits the courtesy if it's an empty one. In this case he truly wants you to come again." He paused for a moment, then went on more softly. "Will you?"

There was that hint of insecurity again, but from Alanna's viewpoint it was easily assuaged. "Of course, I will. That's a foolish thing to ask. I'd love to spend more time with them.

"Have you found any solution to that problem of your father's frustration?" she asked. "He seemed fine tonight."

"He was," Alex agreed, "with *you* as a diversion. I've tried your tactic, but it's going to take some working on." He sighed. "That's another reason for you to come back another time. *You* can work on him!"

Once before, Alex had suggested the same. Then Alanna had promptly and unconditionally ruled out the possibility. Now she did not. How things had changed!

Unfortunately, things had *not* changed when Alanna arrived at work Monday morning. The weekend with Alex had provided lots of bolstering, rest, relaxation and loving. If Alanna was puzzled by Alex's failure to pressure her on the issue of marriage she said nothing, grateful only that, given the continued tension at WallMar, he should be so understanding. There was no doubt in her mind that the visit with his parents on Saturday evening had been a subtle push in the direction of marriage. Oh, yes, his approach had grown more subtle, but it was as potent as ever.

By midweek Alanna had grown more, not less, sensitive to the undercurrent of suspicion aimed at her by the WallMar employees. By week's end she felt near defeat. Regardless of how hard she worked, how strongly she projected the image of professionalism that should have countermanded any other image, there was always that distance, that aloofness on the part of the men with whom she had to deal on an everyday basis. It seemed suddenly much harder to get ideas across, to inspire the support of these people whose help was mandatory to the success of her projects.

"I don't know," she sighed in halfhearted resignation when she and Alex were having dinner Friday night at what had become their favorite spot, a small seafood restaurant on the waterfront. "Maybe I *should* resign. . . ."

His gaze narrowed. "You don't really mean that."

"I do. I'm not sure it's worth the turmoil it's caused."

"Come on, love. That's foolish—"

"But I can't get things done the way I could before. It's gotten to the point of being counterproductive."

"Then *do* something about it!" Alex was suddenly vehement; the shooting sparks of silver in his charcoal eyes told her so, as did the fierce set of his jaw.

"Like . . . ?" She readily sought out his opinion. His suggestions were usually good, particularly when she tempered them with her own instinct. She had, indeed, come to rely on hashing things out with him at night.

"Like stepping things up. Taking the offensive. Confronting the men head-on. Demanding *more* of them. Exerting that power you were given as Executive Vice-President. You have no need to be afraid of them. They're trying to see where their silent form of intimidation will take them. Show them, love. Show them that it won't get them anywhere!"

Dubious, Alanna considered his gentle command for several moments before shifting the subject to something less explosive. Her tension remained intact, however. Sensing it, Alex drove to his apartment, rather than hers, when the meal was over.

"You'd rather stay here tonight?" she asked in surprise. It had become their habit to stay together at Alanna's apartment, where Alex had gradually left a collection of personal items. Perhaps he had felt she would be more comfortable at her own place; for her part, she easily accepted the arrangement, pleased simply to be with him.

"I think," he drawled as he parked and led her from the car, "that you could use the pampering tonight. I have a treat upstairs." Cocking his head in that direction, he seemed suddenly filled with mischief.

"A treat?" Alanna's tone was one of skepticism, then caution. "I'm not so sure about you. Your treats . . . a little pampering . . . so solicitous . . . what is it you want?"

Alex's dark brows drew together as he feigned indignance. "Have I ever bribed you?" When she simply stared at him, trying to camouflage her own humor, he repeated his question. "Have I?"

"Well," she hesitated, "not in so many words." There was bribery and then there was bribery. The lure of his body and the fear of its absence were a form of bribery leading toward marriage, as was a personal involvement with his family. Even the promise of a good night's sleep had its power. "OK, so what's the treat?"

He kept her on tenterhooks as they entered his

building, took the elevator to the top floor, walked down the long hall to his door and then stood while he fumbled with deliberate leisure for his keys.

"Alex . . ." she warned teasingly. "What *is* the treat?"

But this time it was Alex who was saved by the bell. Even before the door was opened the muffled ring of the telephone penetrated its hard wood thickness. And Alex savored the suspense.

"Now who could that be?" he drawled, lazily guiding Alanna over the threshold and ambling toward the phone. She stood not far from him, hands on hips, watching the firm curve of his manly lips as he spoke deeply into the receiver. Then, abruptly, his smile faded.

Instinct told Alanna that something was wrong—something big. Alex was deeply disturbed. His gray gaze shot toward her, then away. He spoke softly, asking questions she couldn't quite follow. With his body angled away from her he seemed to be shielding her from whatever it was that he said. There was a long silence when he finally replaced the receiver. At last he turned toward her, placing his hands on her shoulders, his expression softening slightly.

"What is it?" Alanna asked, eyes wide with worry.

"It's Jake. He's had a heart attack."

Chapter Ten

$\mathcal{A}$ heart attack?" Alanna's hoarse whisper was barely audible, though the tremor of fear that passed through her could not have escaped the awareness of the man who had a strong hold on her shoulders. When disbelief yielded to the look of sorrow on Alex's face she leaned full against him and moaned her anguish. He held her quietly, undemandingly, offering the sheer comfort of his presence until she felt able to learn more.

"When?" She looked up at Alex.

"About two hours ago."

"But I saw him at the office at five."

"It happened shortly after he got home."

Alanna gasped. "Elaine . . . ?"

"Elaine is at the hospital. That was Jake's secretary who called. When there was no answer at your place Elaine suggested she try here."

Alanna's voice was choked for a moment, during which time she could only appreciate the fact that Alex was here with her, offering his silent strength. Finally she spoke falteringly. "Is it bad?"

"He's holding his own, but it was a major attack. The next two or three days will be critical."

Slowly Alanna stepped back from Alex and looked aimlessly around the room, seeming to search for direction in the inanimate objects before her. When that failed her she dug within to find her reserve of levelheadedness. Turning back to Alex, she spoke softly. "I'd like to go to the hospital. Elaine may need some company."

Alex's voice was sympathetic. "I was going to suggest as much. Come on, I'll drive you right over. You'll feel better once you're with Elaine and can see Jake's condition for yourself."

The drive to the hospital seemed endless to Alanna. What would she find when she got there? Jake and Elaine had come to mean so much to her. If something happened to Jake . . .

"Try to relax." Alex urged her gently from her somber preoccupation, giving her hand a squeeze. "Modern medicine can do wonders."

"But he isn't even sixty! There's so much more living for him to do. I don't understand it. . . . He's had no trouble with his heart before! Oh, Alex . . . Elaine needs him so badly!" It was a moment of true weakness for Alanna. Somehow the luxury of having Alex's sturdy figure beside her allowed her to show the feelings, to express the thoughts, that she might otherwise have bottled up. Absurd as it was to argue with him about the improbability of Jake's falling victim to heart disease, she felt the need to voice her frustration and helplessness. Alex recognized that need, as he always seemed able to do.

"Until we hear otherwise, Alanna," he soothed her, "let's try to think positive. Chances for recovery from heart attacks nowadays are excellent. There are new medicines, with more approved every year, to greatly reduce the chances of follow-up attacks."

She pondered his words, clinging desperately to them. "I only hope you're right," she sighed in prayer.

He was. By the end of the weekend Jake's condition had stabilized so much that the prognosis for full recovery was good. Though still in the intensive care unit, he had spoken several times with Alanna, assuring her that he felt better and expressing his concern over Elaine, who stayed with him in the hospital. Alex was a comfort to both women. Alanna, for one, didn't know what she would have done without his ever-present moral support.

On Sunday night, when Alex returned with her to her apartment, where they had spent both previous nights, Alanna was particularly quiet. Jake had spoken of other things shortly before she'd left his room, things she didn't want to face until the morning. As always, Alex sensed her wish, coaxing her into several hours worth of chess before leading her to bed. If he had been troubled that night she was too engrossed in her own thoughts to notice. Yet there was a tenderness to his lovemaking that touched her.

It was as though he spent longer looking, tasting, touching her than ever before, as though some deep need had to be satisfied by a slow reacquaintance. Alanna let herself fall under his spell, gladly seeking out the escape from the world of reality that his impassioned virility demanded. There was something poignant in their coming together that night, something that she would not understand until the following morning, when Alex woke her earlier than usual.

"I have to run now, love." He sounded strangely tired.

Blinking away her own fatigue, she struggled to sit up. He was dressed already. "Why so early, Alex? Is something wrong?"

His smile was sad. "Not really. Well, perhaps. I'm not quite sure."

Startled into alarm by his uncharacteristic waffling, she awoke fully. "What is it?"

"I'm going now." He repeated his first words, but there was a new finality about them. "You've got a very busy day ahead of you."

So, he had guessed what Jake's request had been. She had known he would. "I don't really have a choice, do I?" she whispered. "He's been so good to me. He gave me that very first chance. Now that he's down I've got to fill in for him."

Alex stared intently at her. "Acting President of WallMar Enterprises is nothing to apologize for, love. You'll do just fine." Again there was an uncomfortable hint of farewell in his words, upsetting Alanna far more than the prospect of what faced her at work.

Mustering a steadiness of voice, she asked the question that seemed inevitable. "Will I see you tonight?" And the answer, too, seemed inevitable. It had only been a matter of time.

"Not tonight, Alanna," he said gently, reaching up to trace the gentle line of her cheek.

Her breath caught, making speech difficult. Still she forced herself. "Why not? What is it, Alex? Do you have other plans?"

His charcoal gaze speared her reproachfully. "You know I don't."

"Then why?" She felt as though the rug were being pulled out from under her and she struggled for balance. Yes, she had suspected that the time would come when she would have to make a choice. Wasn't that what she had always feared—the choice between career and love? Alex had told her once that there need not be a choice. Was he changing his stance? But why now, when she needed his support so badly?

As though reading her thoughts once more, Alex sighed, looked straight at her and spoke softly. "I want you to listen to me carefully, love, and don't interrupt. I'm not sure I can repeat this. It's taken me a good part of the night to formulate these thoughts—"

"Then it really is over." She struggled for calm, interrupting him against his orders. "Come the time that you can't *sleep* with me . . ." What might have been humorous once was not so now.

"Listen, Alanna!" he fairly shouted, his own tension written clearly on his beloved features as she scanned them, one by one. "You have a very important period ahead of you. You're right; you really don't have a choice. Jake needs you to take over his job for a month or two until he gets back on his feet." Alanna listened to his words, feeling a chill seep deeper into her with each one. Her protective hand drew the covers up more tightly about her as she leaned against the headboard.

"I think that, during this period, it might be best if we took a break from one another. It's been an intensive few weeks . . ."

"Don't you love me?" Her words were choked off as he interrupted her.

"Of course I love you, Alanna. Nothing can change that." The fierceness of his tone convinced her, yet she couldn't assimilate what he was trying to tell her.

"Then *why?*"

"Because you need time and I've run out of patience. Don't you see, Alanna? I want to marry you. I want you to be my wife, career and all." When she would have jumped to accept out of panic he went determinedly on. "But I *know* you. This is the apex, love. This is the high point, at least one of them, of your career. You need to be able to give it your all, the way you would have a month ago, before you met me. You need to work through this yourself."

Alanna lay frozen, feeling the receding of a world of warmth and beauty, sunshine and sharing that had become a very important part of her. Alex sat by the side of the bed, looking as handsome as ever despite the invisible burden that seemed to weigh him down. Her instinct was to comfort him, to throw herself into his arms in search of that same comfort. Her heart screamed for him, urging her to agree to be his wife, clamoring that she do something, *anything,* to keep him by her side.

Her mind, however, knew Alanna Evans. Her mind knew, likewise, that Alex was right. This was a battle she had to fight on her own if she was ever to come to him with a free heart. It was an awesome challenge. Could she meet it and survive?

The pain of their impending separation edged her voice with a thin, barely wavering timber. "When will I see you?" Her gaze was luminous as it savored every last minute of him.

This, too, he had thought out. "That's up to you, Alanna. Once you get to WallMar today and take over at Jake's desk you're going to be suddenly immersed in corporate business that will demand every bit of your inner resources. I know you can do it; I think you know it, too. But I can't begin to predict when you'll be able to emerge." He paused, studying her with an intensity that spoke of his own immersion in the emotional abyss they shared. "You know where I'll be . . . when you're ready. . . ."

With that he stood and headed for the door. "Alex . . . !" Panic threatened to crumble every defense Alanna thought she'd possessed. Only a last-minute shred of reason held her back. When the tall dark figure turned on the threshold for a final look back she forced a weak smile and an even weaker whisper. "You never did tell what that treat was. . . ."

He had been several steps behind her, totally lost in the act of leaving. Then confusion gentled to indulgence as he shook his head, sighed, then gazed at her a final time. "A sauna. I had a small sauna installed at the apartment. You would have enjoyed it. . . ."

This time when he turned his step did not falter. Alanna's hand flew to her mouth to smother the cry that hovered in her throat. Gone. He was gone. The carpet muffled his footsteps, yet the gentle closing of the front door was as definitive as a gunshot. Gone. *Gone!*

She didn't know how long she sat without moving. On the heels of silence came an acceptance of what had happened. Then came an outpouring of emotion—of trembling, of chills, of utter dejection, of near terror— and a gradual calming as she finally, inevitably, pulled herself together.

He was right. A challenge stood before her which she had to face, once and for all. But Alex had only mentioned half of what was ahead. Yes, there was the challenge of heading WallMar Enterprises and knowing herself to be at the top, the very top, of the ladder. There was also, however, the test of her future. Having sampled life with Alex Knight, now she would relive life alone. *You know where I'll be . . . when you're ready,* he had said. What he hadn't said was that she should come to him only when *she* was ready for that total commitment. Should she find, in the next few weeks, that life at the top held everything she wanted— *without him*—she would be on her own. The implication was clear. He would bother her no more.

A pervasive sense of loneliness maintained a hold on her as she quietly moved from the bed, showered and dressed for the day. She felt strangely numb, as though the same emotions Alex had unleashed with his entrance into her life had now been temporarily erased. Reason alone remained. As she neared the WallMar complex it was reason that took charge, reason that gave her courage, reason that outlined her plan of attack. *Take the offensive,* he had said. *Confront them head-on. Demand more of them. Don't be afraid.*

Chin cocked at an angle of self-assurance, Alanna Evans entered WallMar Enterprises, strode down the long corridor to the office of Jake Wallace, spent several precious moments engrossed in thought and took a deep, deep breath before calling in the staff who now worked for her. Hands clenched on the arms of her chair, where no one could see them, she addressed them quietly, deliberately, forcefully.

"There are twelve of us here," she began, looking from one to the other the sometimes curious, sometimes skeptical, sometimes openly antagonistic faces of the men who were sharing the office with her, some standing, some lounging against window sills and some sitting in the few scattered chairs. "It's up to the twelve of us to keep WallMar Enterprises moving, and moving *forward,* during Jake's recovery." In a momentary diversion she softened, explaining the latest on Jake Wallace's condition as the hospital had reported it to her shortly before she'd left her apartment. That, however, was the extent of the amenities she offered. When she paused for a breath, then began again, there was a strength, a maturity in her voice that perked up even the most irreverent ears in the room.

"Let me begin by saying," her gaze was steady, "that I am well aware of the skepticism many of you feel, and the resentment. Without stooping to answer the ludicrous charges that have already been made against me in the past I would like to move forward. Standing in Jake's shoes may be the greatest challenge I'll ever face.

Here is *your* opportunity *and* mine. I'm prepared to prove that I've earned my right to stand before you. If I fail now you may believe what you want. But if I succeed I will demand your respect." Pausing for a moment, she forced her hands to relax, folding them on the desk before her.

"Unfortunately," her tone was even as she continued, "I can't run WallMar Enterprises on my own. I'll need all your help. You are indispensible to this organization . . . and to me. However," her gaze narrowed behind the tinted lenses, "if I find that any one of you refuses to give his all I will have no compunction whatsoever in dismissing him." An imperceptible stirring passed through the group; they had not expected such a speech. "Are there any questions?"

When there seemed to be no immediate rebellion Alanna felt that she had won a minor victory. Minor . . . but a victory nonetheless. "Fine, then. I'm already familiar with the general workings of each of your departments. Now I need to hear the details as Jake knows them. You will all have somewhat more responsibility than you may have had before because I simply cannot shoulder it all at the start. But I would like to meet with each of you today, starting with you, Craig," she eyed the chief of marketing, "at ten. I want you to tell me exactly what your department is up to right now, what's pending for the week, what problems need immediate attention. There will be some overlap and much of what you say I may be familiar with. But I don't want to miss any bases. Understood?"

Amid the nods and low-murmured words of agreement there were no outward signs of complaint. There were questions from several, suggestions from one or two, but Alanna was able to handle them all with remarkable skill. She had passed the first hurdle; Alex would have been proud. Yes, there was a definite tension existing among this group, but that was inevitable. It would be a time of testing, as she had told them. She would be on trial—in their eyes, in Jake's eyes, in her own eyes. As for Alex, some deep, private instinct told her of his faith in her. It was the knowledge of this faith that had given her the strength to face these men, some of whom might well be hostile beneath the skin. Alex would be with her, she knew, in both mind and heart throughout this trial. His presence in her life had affected her deeply; his physical absence now could not rob her of the memories of richness, warmth and love, all of which stood behind her as she faced this professional challenge.

Time and again as the days passed she asked herself if she was ready to call him. Despite her preoccupation with WallMar Enterprises, he was never far from her mind. Could she agree to his terms? Could she agree to become his wife, to bear his children, to share her career? And time and again she saw the wisdom of Alex's distance. It was simply too easy the other way . . . too easy to go on indefinitely loving and enjoying without further commitment. Painful as it was, he had been right. Until every last doubt was erased from her mind she had to remain alone.

The siege lasted for a month. During that time Alanna learned more about WallMar Enterprises than she had ever dreamed possible. By the end of the first week, she had the cooperation, albeit at times reluctant, of the men she had confronted that first day. By the end of the second week she had their cautious and conditional enthusiasm. By the end of the third week she had their reluctant respect. From there it was free sailing.

The last week, in particular, was painful for Alanna. She had neither heard from nor seen Alex and she missed him terribly. Despite her gruelling schedule she thought of him constantly. There was little time in the twelve hours a day spent at the office for personal considerations, or during the hour or two spent each evening with Jake and Elaine, first at the hospital, then at their home after Jake was discharged. Each night— each long, sleep-disturbed night—was devoted to Alex.

It was a time of soul-searching. Yes, she missed him. But what, exactly, did she miss? She missed his quiet company at the end of each day, his unfailing support, his eager enthusiasm. She missed the sounding board that he had become to her in such a very short time. She missed, to her astonishment, his sense of protectiveness, even the possessiveness she might have minded in the past. She missed his smile, his eyes, his hands and chest and shoulders. And she missed the way he made her feel—complete and satisfied—in his arms.

Sleep was an elusive quality once more. Alex's lovemaking had exhausted her physically, but there had been far more to it than that. More even than exhaustion, the secret of her deep sleep in Alex's arms was contentment, peace, a sense of safety. It was the knowledge that he loved her, that he needed her, that he wanted to spend the rest of his life with her.

Out of sight he was. Certainly not out of mind. He filled her senses, her thoughts, her heart, her deepest, most secret core. The pain of missing him was invisible, intangible and absolutely excruciating. And it grew daily, a bristly weed among the daisies. It was a thorn in her side, embedding itself deeper and deeper. It was a blotch on an otherwise astounding report card. It was a gaping void craving fulfillment.

By the end of that fourth week, having convinced herself, her co-workers, and Jake of the smooth and forward progress of the business under her direction, the moment of truth was at hand. She had done it, had proven what she had set out to prove. As Acting President of WallMar Enterprises she had won the respect of the skeptics. Through action, rather than words, she had disproven the scandalous claims of that now-distant newspaper article. Yet she still faced the moment of truth, the moment when there was no longer any question in her mind.

The nights, long nights of loneliness, had painted dark smudges beneath her eyes. The days, long days of work, had left her satisfied, yet not satisfied. When she found herself with her hand on the phone, as it had been nearly every night that month, she knew she could wait no longer. It was a matter of simple honesty. Honesty to herself. Honesty to Alex. Honesty to the love they shared.

"Hello?" His voice was deep and low, sending an instant bolt of pleasure through her. Yet suddenly emotion choked off all sound. Emotion—that same emotion that had gone unexpressed, that had kept her up, night after night—now welled with frightening force. "Hello?" Alex repeated the word, challenging her, this last time, to respond.

"Alex . . . ?" she whispered. There was no sound from the other end of the wire. "Alex . . . can I see you?" When there was still no response, she panicked. Had he changed his mind, after all? "Alex?"

"I'm here, love." He spoke thickly, the distancing effect of the telephone disguising the depth of his own emotion. "Are you ready?"

There was the question, the thought connecting past with present, present with future.

Alanna had no doubts. "I'm ready. I'm on my way to your place. Will you . . . will you . . . ?" *Be there* seemed far too maudlin. "Will you . . . heat up the sauna?"

Later they would both laugh at the improbable location for a reunion and the spontaneity with which the thought of it had popped to her mind. For now, emotion ran far too high for humor.

"It's hot and waiting, Alanna," his thick tones beckoned. Without a second thought, Alanna headed home.

It was not the sauna that took first priority upon her arrival at his apartment. Rather, it was the pair of arms that folded her to him, the voice that whispered words of love in her ear, the tall, dark man who held her away from him to drink in her presence as she devoured his.

"Talk to me, Alanna," he ordered softly, leading her to the sofa and sitting beside her. "Before anything happens I need you to tell me what's changed in that mind of yours to bring you here."

But Alanna was too drugged with love to want to talk. Reaching for him, she locked her arms about him, seeking his heartbeat, savoring it until he set her back purposefully. "Can't we talk later, Alex?" she whispered, craning to kiss the rugged line of his jaw.

That old, familiar eyebrow arched. "I dare you to talk *now*, love. Let's see what kind of self-control you *really* have!"

"Alex! That's unfair," she chided in soft frustration. Every nerve end craved his touch, every sense cried for his possession. But at the moment Alex's need for the words he'd waited so long to hear was far greater. The vulnerability in his expression told her that. He had been free and open with his feelings from the start; it was only fair that, now that she finally understood her own more clearly, she share them.

"I love you," she whispered, though she dropped her arms in acquiescence.

"What else is new?" There was a barbed resignation in his tone.

For a moment she pondered it. "I deserved that. I *have* been . . . stubborn, haven't I?"

"Uh-huh." The smiled that toyed with the corners of his lips was genuine. Glorying in it, she found herself spurred on.

"I'm ready, Alex, ready to make that commitment."

"Why?"

"Because I love you."

When he shook his dark head she was taken aback.

"Not good enough," he announced firmly. "You've loved me for some time now. What makes you suddenly want marriage?"

As she looked into his eyes she saw those silver sparkles, held in abeyance, waiting to burst forth. On impulse, and quite inappropriately, she grinned. "You know, when I was a little girl I had a game that worked with wires and batteries. It was a quiz game, question-and-answer type thing. If you made the right connection the red light went on." Mischief sparkled in her own eyes as slowly, slowly she felt the chill that had occupied her body since the morning Alex had left begin to dissipate.

"What on earth does that have to do with anything?" the cause of the thaw growled deeply.

"It means that your eyes will be my reward when I give the correct answer. Your silver sparkles . . . they're waiting. . . ."

"I'm waiting," he reminded her in warning.

At that instant, abruptly sobering, Alanna knew that it was time to end the waiting. For them both. Forever. "These four weeks have been an experience I needed, Alex. They've opened my eyes in many ways." When she reached for his hand he allowed her to take it, yet he sat silent, waiting. "You were right when you insisted I do it alone. I've lived my whole adult life that way. If I hadn't done it alone now I might always have wondered, wondered whether I had it in me, whether I might have made it, whether I would have been sufficient to the task and whether it would have been enough for me."

"And?" His features finally began to relax. Suddenly

Alanna found her hand covered by his in a subtle but meaningful turnaround.

"No, it wasn't. I've seen the top of the ladder, reached the heights I'd hoped, in my wildest dreams, to reach. And no, it wasn't enough. I've learned that I can make it, that I can be *president* if I want. But I don't." She sighed, nearing the end of her control. "These past four weeks have been the busiest I've ever lived through. But I've never been as lonely in my entire life." His image blurred before her as her eyes suddenly filled with tears. "I need you, Alex. I need to be with you, to know that you're here when I come home, to be here for you. That world out there has no meaning unless you're in it with me."

A solitary tear trickled down her pale cheek as Alex drew her against him, ending their separation for all time. "I've missed you, owl-eyes," he groaned, hugging her tightly, absorbing her memories of pain and loneliness and unfulfilled desire, exorcising his own in the process. "These have been the worst days I ever hope to spend."

Alanna turned her luminous cocoa gaze to his features. Now she saw them clearly—the exhaustion, the strain, the drawn look that must have mirrored her own.

"You did wait," she whispered in awe, daring to voice that one most devastating fear for the time spent apart.

"Of course I waited! Did you think I wouldn't?"

"I tried *not* to think of that possibility. You do have the patience of a saint."

"Patience, love, had nothing to do with it. I damn

near lost my mind wondering when you'd come to your senses."

"You were that sure?" she asked skeptically.

His response held no skepticism at all. "I was." Then he smiled. "It's been very hard for a man like me, a person who sees what he wants and goes after it, to sit back and wait for what he wants to come after him."

"Why did you?"

A month of asking himself the same question provided the ready answer. "I did it because the prize was worth it. You've come to me now with that much *more* inside you. And I love you all the more for it."

His words brought a reappearance of the tears that had temporarily dried. Gently he lifted the oversized glasses from the bridge of her nose, then kissed the teardrop from each eye in turn. Her forehead, her cheeks, her nose . . . all received the blessing of his kiss. But her lips, warm and open, eager and inviting, waited. . . .

"Alex!" Exasperated, she took matters into her hands, thrusting her fingers through his hair to the fine-trimmed thatch at the nape of his neck, drawing his face toward hers until, at last, in a moment of mind-shattering triumph, he kissed her.

Alanna had never felt as complete as when those lips slanted hungrily across hers, opening and mastering her mouth with a power that thrilled her. When the tip of his tongue strayed deeper she felt charged with an energy she had lacked since that last, poignant night a month ago.

Suddenly anything, *everything*, in life was possible. The world was hers. Happiness soared through her as a dove before the sun, pure and fresh and sparkling. She felt fully alive and keenly aware, sizzling from head to toe with the force of a love that would be restrained no longer.

How it all burst forth as it did she would never know. But there was suddenly a frenzy of activity, a melange of hands and arms, of fingers fumbling with buttons. With unrestrained abandon they left a trail of clothing strewn behind, a trail of shirts, of skirt and trousers, bra, slip, briefs, panties . . . all leading toward the bathroom, where they moved, as one, toward the sauna.

The sauna . . . a breath of heat from the desert, instantly slowing life to a more languorous pace, toasting all within its reach. As Alex sat on the lone wood bench Alanna stood before him, reaching unhurriedly to touch his face, to smooth the dark hair back from his brow. Theirs was a world in isolation, a golden world lit by a warm and glowing sun.

He spread his knees and drew her between them, resting his head against the gentle harbor of her breasts. His hands stroked her from shoulder to hip, drawing lazy circles to call forth tremors from deep within her. Overflowing with an emotional ecstasy, she trembled at the physical bounty offered by this man's body, the sinewed strength beneath her tapered fingertips.

"Aaaaah," she moaned, a hoarse sound from deep in her throat as she tipped her head back in delight allowing long, blond tangles to cascade over his fingers. "I've missed you, too, Alex. How I've missed you!"

Her hands clasped against the corded mass of his

shoulders, her head dipped forward once more, this time to meet the lips that waited to return the message of love and elaborate on it. In one fluid stroke Alex's hands slid behind her, lifting her, drawing her close until she felt the strength of him that was her power as well. Yet he prolonged the moment, adoring her features with his gaze, then his hands. His man-rough fingers slid easily and with fiery touch around her shoulders to her chest and her breasts, pausing only briefly to tantalize buds that were taut with desire before searing a path lower.

Breath came in ragged gasps for them both as they struggled to express all the thoughts bubbling forth from the heady cauldron of passion.

"I love you, Alanna. . . ."

"I love you, too. . . ."

A flurry of kisses momentarily put a stop to conversation.

"Have you been able to sleep?" he asked, nibbling at her earlobe, his chest rising and falling rapidly.

"No. Have you?"

His fingers delved deeper and she moaned, but he ignored her cry. "Not once . . . through the night. . . ."

The tide of passion carried them higher. Alanna strained closer. "I never knew what I was missing . . . until you came along. . . ." she whispered. This time it was Alex who moaned.

For Alanna that moment was the true pinnacle of her dream of success and happiness. The body that glistened beneath her, before her, was only the start. She stroked it lovingly, mesmerized by the play of rippling muscles and the beaded moisture over its dark, hair-roughened skin.

As Alex shifted her, lifted her, then possessed her in one rapturous motion she cried out her love, then cried no more. For it was a time of living and loving, of sharing and creating. Alex was her equal, her friend. He was her helpmate, her partner. He was her lover; he would be her husband. Through his vision she had glimpsed a future more rich in meaning than anything she had ever conceived of. With him, and only him, she might have that future.

It would be filled with a fine blend of career and family, with Alex beside her all the way. It would have the same ups and downs, the same highs and lows as all of existence had. But it was special, unique, the challenge of a lifetime. Alanna accepted it eagerly.

Genuine Silhouette
sterling silver bookmark
for only $15.95!

What a beautiful way to hold your place in your current romance! This genuine sterling silver bookmark, with the distinctive Silhouette symbol in elegant black, measures 1½″ long and 1″ wide. It makes a beautiful gift for yourself, and for every romantic you know! And, at only $15.95 each, including all postage and handling charges, you'll want to order several now, while supplies last.

Send your name and address with check or money order for $15.95 per bookmark ordered to
Simon & Schuster Enterprises
120 Brighton Rd., P.O. Box 5020
Clifton, N.J. 07012
Attn: Bookmark

Bookmarks can be ordered pre-paid only. No charges will be accepted. Please allow 4-6 weeks for delivery.

N.Y. State Residents
Please Add Sales Tax

Silhouette Special Edition

MORE ROMANCE FOR
A SPECIAL WAY TO RELAX

$1.95 each

1 ☐ TERMS OF SURRENDER Dailey
2 ☐ INTIMATE STRANGERS Hastings
3 ☐ MEXICAN RHAPSODY Dixon
4 ☐ VALAQUEZ BRIDE Vitek
5 ☐ PARADISE POSTPONED Converse
6 ☐ SEARCH FOR A NEW DAWN Douglass
7 ☐ SILVER MIST Stanford
8 ☐ KEYS TO DANIEL'S HOUSE Halston
9 ☐ ALL OUR TOMORROWS Baxter
10 ☐ TEXAS ROSE Thiels
11 ☐ LOVE IS SURRENDER Thornton
12 ☐ NEVER GIVE YOUR HEART Sinclair
13 ☐ BITTER VICTORY Beckman
14 ☐ EYE OF THE HURRICANE Keene
15 ☐ DANGEROUS MAGIC James
16 ☐ MAYAN MOON Carr
17 ☐ SO MANY TOMORROWS John
18 ☐ A WOMAN'S PLACE Hamilton
19 ☐ DECEMBER'S WINE Shaw
20 ☐ NORTHERN LIGHTS Musgrave
21 ☐ ROUGH DIAMOND Hastings

22 ☐ ALL THAT GLITTERS Howard
23 ☐ LOVE'S GOLDEN SHADOW Charles
24 ☐ GAMBLE OF DESIRE Dixon
25 ☐ TEARS AND RED ROSES Hardy
26 ☐ A FLIGHT OF SWALLOWS Scott
27 ☐ A MAN WITH DOUBTS Wisdom
28 ☐ THE FLAMING TREE Ripy
29 ☐ YEARNING OF ANGELS Bergen
30 ☐ BRIDE IN BARBADOS Stephens
31 ☐ TEARS OF YESTERDAY Baxter
32 ☐ A TIME TO LOVE Douglass
33 ☐ HEATHER'S SONG Palmer
34 ☐ MIXED BLESSING Sinclair
35 ☐ STORMY CHALLENGE James
36 ☐ FOXFIRE LIGHT Dailey
37 ☐ MAGNOLIA MOON Stanford
38 ☐ WEB OF PASSION John
39 ☐ AUTUMN HARVEST Milan
40 ☐ HEARTSTORM Converse
41 ☐ COLLISION COURSE Halston
42 ☐ PROUD VINTAGE Drummond

Silhouette Special Edition

MORE ROMANCE FOR A SPECIAL WAY TO RELAX

43 ☐ ALL SHE EVER WANTED Shaw
44 ☐ SUMMER MAGIC Eden
45 ☐ LOVE'S TENDER TRIAL Charles
46 ☐ AN INDEPENDENT WIFE Howard
47 ☐ PRIDE'S POSSESSION Stephens
48 ☐ LOVE HAS ITS REASONS Ferrell
49 ☐ A MATTER OF TIME Hastings
50 ☐ FINDERS KEEPERS Browning
51 ☐ STORMY AFFAIR Trent

52 ☐ DESIGNED FOR LOVE Sinclair
53 ☐ GODDESS OF THE MOON Thomas
54 ☐ THORNE'S WAY Hohl
55 ☐ SUN LOVER Stanford
56 ☐ SILVER FIRE Wallace
57 ☐ PRIDE'S RECKONING Thornton
58 ☐ KNIGHTLY LOVE Douglass
59 ☐ THE HEART'S VICTORY Roberts
60 ☐ ONCE AND FOREVER Thorne

LOOK FOR *AFTER THE RAIN* BY LINDA SHAW AVAILABLE IN JANUARY AND *SEASON OF SEDUCTION* BY ABRA TAYLOR IN FEBRUARY.

SILHOUETTE SPECIAL EDITION, Department SE/2
1230 Avenue of the Americas
New York, NY 10020

Please send me the books I have checked above. I am enclosing $_____
(please add 50¢ to cover postage and handling. NYS and NYC residents
please add appropriate sales tax). Send check or money order—no cash or
C.O.D.'s please. Allow six weeks for delivery.

NAME _____

ADDRESS _____

CITY _____ STATE/ZIP _____

Silhouette Special Edition

Coming Next Month

Tender Deception by Patti Beckman

After the crash, memory gone and appearance altered, Lilly Parker began to search for her identity and found Kirk, her husband . . . who had fallen in love with the woman she'd become!

Deep Waters by Laurey Bright

Dallas fought her attraction for anthropologist, Nick, from the steaming jungles of Engima Island to the moon-silvered beaches . . . but where he was concerned she knew she would be easily conquered.

Love With A Perfect Stranger by Pamela Wallace

One night aboard the Orient Express they met— and carried away by romance, Torey gave her heart. Now, trip over, Peter West would leave her life forever . . . or would he?

Mist Of Blossoms by Jane Converse

Singing star Brett Wells was tired of being chased by women. So how could Carolyn tell him of her love when he insisted that they remain just friends?

Handful Of Sky by Tory Cates

Shallie had to make her way in rodeo, a man's world, and Hunt McIver's help was invaluable. But the man himself remained a mystery . . . one she longed to solve.

A Sporting Affair by Jennifer Mikels

Alaine's heart never had so much as a sporting chance of escaping unscathed once she met ballplayer Doug Morrow, the charismatic pitcher who made it clear he would have things his own way.

Silhouette 💫 *Romance*

15-Day Free Trial Offer
6 Silhouette Romances

6 Silhouette Romances, free for 15 days! We'll send you 6 new Silhouette Romances to keep for 15 days, absolutely free! If you decide not to keep them, send them back to us. You pay nothing.

Free Home Delivery. But if you enjoy them as much as we think you will, keep them by paying the invoice enclosed with your free trial shipment. We'll pay all shipping and handling charges. You get the convenience of Home Delivery and we pay the postage and handling charge each month.

Don't miss a copy. The Silhouette Book Club is the way to make sure you'll be able to receive every new romance we publish before they're sold out. There is no minimum number of books to buy and you can cancel at any time.

This offer expires June 30, 1983

Silhouette Book Club, Dept. SRSE 7B
120 Brighton Road, Clifton, NJ 07012

Please send me 6 Silhouette Romances to keep for 15 days, absolutely free. I understand I am not obligated to join the Silhouette Book Club unless I decide to keep them.

NAME_____

ADDRESS_____

CITY_____ STATE_____ ZIP_____